*A
Harlequin
Romance*

OTHER

Harlequin Romances

by LUCY GILLEN

A TOUCH OF HONEY

by

LUCY GILLEN

HARLEQUIN BOOKS   TORONTO
WINNIPEG

Harlequin edition published September 1975

SBN 373-01908-4

Original hard cover edition published in 1973
Mills & Boon Limited

Printed in Canada

CHAPTER ONE

CADIE looked at the fat white clouds rolling lazily across a blue sky that was much too bright and sunny to take their threat seriously. If this was Dorly Creek she was going to enjoy being here.

She was not familiar with this part of the coast, but she had heard quite a lot about it from Dottie, who had gone into raptures over it, taking up almost a page of letter to sing its praises. Of course one had to take into account the fact that Dottie was quite newly married and that Dorly Creek was Michael's home. Even so it looked every bit as good as she had described it, and quite idyllic in the hot July sun.

A wide sweep of golden sand curved round to form the creek that gave the place its name, and the houses dotted around the inlet of blue water with its population of bobbing boats gave it almost a continental air.

Cadie smiled to herself in anticipation of seeing Dottie again. They had been friends at school and later, working in the same office for quite a time. Then Dottie, by a marvellous stroke of luck, had landed the job of secretary to Robert Dean, the playwright.

She had left London and moved down to Dorly Creek where, a couple of months later, she had met and married Michael. Now she was expecting her first baby and, by a bit of unashamed string-pulling, had persuaded her employer to take on Cadie in her place.

Robert Dean's plays were not always to Cadie's taste, but he wrote a lot for television and he was reputed to be one of the cleverest, and wealthiest, of the younger writers. Dottie had loved working for him and she had assured Cadie that she would too.

'Come for a week-end,' Dottie had written, 'and let him give you the once-over, love, then you can give up that dreary job in town and move down here. There's a lovely little cottage we've found for you, that won't cost you the earth in rent.'

Cadie had felt rather dubious about it at first. Being recommended for the job by Dottie meant inevitably that she had been over-sold and heaven knows what the poor man was expecting. She had succumbed to Dottie's insistence, however, and here she was on her way to see Robert Dean, and feeling slightly sick at the prospect of his not liking her.

She had no fears that her qualifications would not suit him, but being a secretary in this capacity was very much different from being part of a big firm. It was a much more personal association and it was essential that there should be no clash of personalities or it would be impossible.

If she was truthful Cadie would have been the first to admit that her attention was wandering as she drove round a corner, following the curve of the creek as it turned inland. She was preoccupied and so unconscious of her surroundings that she gave an audible cry when a second later the strident blare of a car horn

6

startled her, and she braked hard.

Her little car was nose to nose with an enormous great shiny monster that seemed to have appeared out of nowhere, and its driver was even now striding across towards her. He looked more resigned than angry and he sighed as he peered in the window at her.

'A woman driver,' he said gloomily. 'I might have known, I suppose.'

It so happened that he could not have chosen a worse thing to say, for if there was one thing that really incensed Cadie it was the popular male view that all women drivers were hopeless, and she flushed a bright angry pink as she glared at the offender through the open window.

'Sex has no bearing on driving ability whatsoever,' she informed him haughtily, and tightened her soft mouth ominously when he laughed.

How dared he laugh like that? So obviously scornful and all-knowing! She was very tempted to wind up the window and trap the hand that rested there, and only just resisted it. Such blatant discrimination always brought out the feminist in her, although she was not normally militant.

'You could be right,' he said, unexpectedly agreeable. 'But if it had been another man who came round that corner on the wrong side of the road, at least I could have indulged myself and hit him on the nose.'

Cadie curled her lip, her eyes scornful. 'Typical!' she declared, and he laughed again.

'You *are* on the wrong side of the road,' he pointed out. 'Or hadn't you noticed?'

It was true, Cadie noticed with dismay. At least it was partly true, for she was well in the centre of the road, and must have taken the corner far too wide. In the circumstances, she supposed, she should apologize to him, although after his initial remark she was tempted not to.

'I – I didn't realize,' she confessed, and lowered her eyes before the amused but interested gaze that regarded her steadily. 'I'm sorry.'

She was a very attractive girl, and used to admiration from men, but there was something so blatantly speculative about this one's interest that she felt a sudden increase in her pulse rate and dared not look at him.

No man could fail to be impressed, and certainly this one was no different. Black silky hair framed an oval face and flowed down her back to well past her shoulders, kept in place by a slide on top of her head. Her eyes were a deep, fathomless blue and black-fringed with lashes that owed nothing to artifice. The soft mouth, now appealingly parted, seemed to hold his attention longest, and he leaned nearer as he answered.

'If you're really sorry,' he told her, 'I won't do anything about it this time. But don't let me bump into your little sardine can round any more corners or I may not feel so charitable again.'

'I *have* apologized,' Cadie said shortly, 'and you have no call to make disparaging remarks about my car.'

'Oh, I beg your pardon.'

8

'So you should,' Cadie told him, resenting the hint of patronage in his tone.

'Now we've both apologized,' he said, and smiled, and she noticed, irrelevantly, how white his teeth looked against a brown face. He must live here to have acquired such a tan, for the rest of his colouring ruled out any suggestion that it was racial darkness.

He had fair, almost blond hair, and light grey eyes that still watched her amusedly. His height was such that he was obliged to bend almost double to see into the window of her little car, and she wished she felt less like a small child being let off lightly by teacher.

'If you want my name and address to make a report—' she began, but he shook his head and laughed again.

'Not this time,' he told her lightly, 'although I must admit I'm tempted by my curiosity to know who you are. However,' he laughed again at her frown of annoyance, 'I'll let you off as a first offender.'

'Thank you.' Her sarcasm was mild, but he shook his head over it and smiled.

'That's O.K. But don't try to mix dreaming about the boy-friends with driving in future, it's dangerous.'

'Why, of all the—' Cadie glared at him, furiously speechless, then she took off the brake suddenly and shot backward, changing gear noisily.

'Ooh!' He put his hands to his ears, she noticed in her rear mirror, but she was past caring and she drove past the shiny monster, almost brushing one of its gleaming wings as she went. She hated its smug, shiny

9

ostentation as much as she did its owner.

By the time she had found Mercer Avenue where Dottie lived, she had recovered some of her temper, and she looked out for Dottie's house as she drove along slowly. All the gates of the neat, detached houses bore numbers and she easily found number twelve, drawing up outside the white picket gate.

Almost before she had time to close the car door Dottie was out of the house and chattering away excitedly. 'You look gorgeous!' she enthused. 'Absolutely gorgeous, but you always did make me feel plain Jane. Come on in and see Michael, he'll come and get your stuff later.'

Cadie was urged along the short, paved path to the front door, scarcely needing to say anything because Dottie was always quite happy chattering away, even if no one answered her. She already looked pleasantly plump and her round face beamed happiness and good health. There was, Cadie thought, a kind of beauty about her, even if it wasn't immediately recognizable.

Michael Peters, her husband, came forward, hand outstretched, a tolerant smile on his nice, ordinary face. 'Hello, Cadie, how are you?'

'Fine, thanks, Michael.' She let him take her light jacket and put a settling hand to her hair. 'It's lovely and hot, isn't it?'

'Too hot for Dorothy,' Michael said. He never used his wife's nickname. 'She's feeling it a bit, aren't you, darling?'

'I'm sagging at the knees a bit,' Dottie confessed,

although she showed no signs of it.

'You look fine,' Cadie told her, and smiled affectionately at her. 'A little larger perhaps, but fine.'

Dottie put supporting hands to her tummy and grinned. 'It's awful, isn't it?' she asked, obviously meaning no such thing.

'Not at all,' Cadie told her. 'And I'm delighted for you, Dottie.' Her smile encompassed Michael too. 'You too, Michael, you must be very happy, both of you.'

'Oh, we are,' Dottie assured her enthusiastically. 'You should get married, Cadie, it's marvellous.' Her bright brown eyes looked at her friend speculatively. 'Why *aren't* you married by now?' she demanded, and Cadie laughed.

'I suppose because I've never met anybody yet that I felt like spending the rest of my life with,' she said. 'And right now I'm rather off men.'

'Oh?' Dottie looked interested, and Michael smiled ruefully as he went out to fetch Cadie's luggage.

'I've just met one of your local gentry,' Cadie explained, pulling a face. 'I took a corner rather wide and came face to face with a huge monster of a car. The driver was just about the last word in male bigotry and we had words.'

'Oh dear!'

'He very magnanimously let me off with a warning,' Cadie told her, feeling a brief flash of anger again when she remembered the incident. 'Oh, I could cheerfully have slain him!'

'I know the type,' Dottie sympathized. 'I always feel

like batting them on the head with something.'

'I nearly did,' Cadie admitted. 'Only it wouldn't have proved anything, except that I was stupid, as he obviously suspected I was. Oh well,' she added with a wry smile, 'let's hope I never have the misfortune to bump into him again, literally or otherwise, or I might just be tempted to follow my inclinations.'

'Let's hope not,' Dottie echoed. 'There's one thing, love, you won't have any trouble with Robert. He's a pet, and he's marvellous to work for.'

'I'm seeing him tomorrow morning,' Cadie told her, 'and I must admit I'm shaking in my shoes at the idea of meeting him. Suppose he doesn't like me?'

'Oh, he will!' Dottie assured her with conviction. 'He'll adore you, Cadie.'

'I don't want him to adore me,' Cadie demurred. 'Just like me enough to give me the job – I've quite set my heart on it now I've seen Dorly Creek.'

'You don't have to worry. You'll get it easily enough. He loves beauties like you and he's no idea how glam you are. I thought I'd let you be a nice surprise for him.'

Cadie pulled a face. 'Let's hope it's not too *much* of a surprise,' she said.

It seemed strange to be going for an interview at a private house, and Cadie fought to hide a dismaying nervousness that made her throat dry and formed a cold little weight in the pit of her stomach.

Dorly House was impossible to miss, so Dottie had informed her, and it was hardly worth taking the car on such a lovely morning when the walk would do her so much more good.

She had dressed in a businesslike but not too severe outfit of blue and white – a dress with long, transparent sleeves and a demurely high neck, and blue shoes that showed off her slim legs and ankles to their best advantage. She had never worn her hair up and Dottie had assured her that Robert Dean would have absolutely no objection to it as it was.

Her deep blue eyes possibly looked a little wide and anxious as she walked along the stone quay towards the top of the creek where Dorly House stood. She could see the house just ahead of her now, half hidden by the shady pines that partly surrounded it, and she put an anxious hand to her hair and another to smooth her dress as she neared the gates.

Dorly House was painted in black on the white wood and the gates stood invitingly open, the gravel drive curving slightly so that the front of the house was not visible until she had walked another couple of yards or so.

It was big. The biggest house in the district, Dottie had informed her, and she thought how peaceful and attractive it looked in the sunshine, its south and west walls shadowed by the guardian conifers.

The garden was simply but beautifully laid out and had an air of tranquillity that was quite enchanting. Cadie smiled as she walked along the drive, although she had no idea what induced it, except the sheer peace and beauty of the place.

She had almost reached the porch that protected the

front door before she recognized the car standing on the drive, and when she did she stopped short, her eyes doubtful. It would be just her luck if her antagonist of yesterday proved to be a friend of Robert Dean's.

She could only hope that the man was only a casual caller and not a friend likely to influence the great man's opinion. Nevertheless she found her knees horribly unsteady as she went up the two steps to the front door, which was standing ajar.

No one came for so long that she began to wonder if her ring had gone unheard, then suddenly the opening widened and a man blinked at her for a second as if the sight of her startled him.

'I thought I saw someone from the window,' he said. 'I'm terribly sorry if you've been ringing. We're all out in the garden, I'm afraid, and Mrs. Calthrop's out.'

'I've only rung once,' Cadie assured him, putting on her nicest smile to counteract anything her antagonist of yesterday might say. 'I've only just come.'

'Oh, good. Please come in.' He held the door wide and smiled as she passed him. 'Will you come this way?' He turned suddenly and looked embarrassed. 'You *are* Miss O'Connor, aren't you?' he asked, smiling apologetically. 'I should have asked.'

Cadie nodded. 'Yes, I am.'

'In here.'

He led the way into a long, narrow room with a window at each end and a desk by each window. It looked business like but homely too, and she thought she would enjoy working here. Obviously this was where the writing was done, and she felt infinitely more optimistic about getting the job now that she had met this quiet but quite charming man.

She could not quite agree with Dottie's over-enthusiastic description of him as gorgeous, but he was passably good-looking and very, very nice. Not a bit as she had expected him to be, somehow.

'Please sit down, Miss O'Connor.' He indicated a chair on one side of the farther desk and seated himself opposite to her. He was obviously ill at ease and she thought he was nervous about interviewing her. 'Dottie spoke so often about you,' he told her. 'I almost feel as if I know you.'

'Oh, did she?' Dottie had done some advance publicity on her behalf, she knew, and Cadie felt rather embarrassed about it now that she was brought face to face with the fact. 'I – I hope she didn't overdo the enthusiasm and give you the wrong impression.'

'Not at all,' he told her. 'In fact she didn't forewarn us.' He smiled at her. 'She didn't say how – how lovely you were, Miss O'Connor, and that was quite a surprise.'

'Thank you, Mr. Dean.'

He looked quite unduly startled, she thought, and then he shook his head. 'I'm sorry,' he said. 'I should have introduced myself. I'm Gordon Charles, Rob's stepbrother and sometime collaborator.'

'Oh, I beg your pardon.' She could feel the colour in her cheeks and wished she had been less impulsive in presuming his identity. Dottie had told her that Robert Dean's stepbrother lived at Dorly House with him, as did his father, but she had automatically assumed that the man who came to interview her would be Robert Dean himself; now it seemed he had delegated the task to someone else.

'It was my fault entirely,' he hastened to assure her. 'Rob asked me to see you because he's busy at the moment.' That nice friendly smile beamed at her again and Cadie thought it would be quite impossible to be annoyed with him about anything, even if he was very obviously lying. Apparently Robert Dean could not be bothered to see her himself, but from the way in which his stepbrother made the excuse it was evident he was not busy.

'I'm sorry, Mr. Charles,' she said. 'I didn't realize.'

'Of course you didn't.' He leaned forward in his chair, perched uncomfortably on the very edge of the seat. 'I don't know how much Dottie has told you about the job, Miss O'Connor,' he said, 'but I expect she's told you most of the important things.'

'She's talked about it enough,' Cadie agreed with a smile. 'She loved working here and she says I will too. If I'm to have the job, of course,' she added hastily, and he nodded.

'Oh, I don't see why not,' he told her. 'It can be pretty hectic at times when there's a deadline to meet, or it can be very quiet. It's not a normal run-of-the-mill secretarial job as you might expect, but it won't tie you too much to your desk to the exclusion of anything else, and Rob's a *very* considerate employer most of the time.'

She smiled at the qualification. 'That's pretty much

as it always is, Mr. Charles.'

'Oh, good.' He looked relieved, and she thought he was wondering what to say next.

'You'll want to know what I've done before,' she said, coming to his rescue. 'Won't you?'

'Will I? Oh, yes, of course.' He pulled a face at her and smiled, wryly. 'You'll have gathered that I've never interviewed anyone before, Miss O'Connor, but please don't blame me, will you?'

'I won't,' Cadie promised, returning the smile. 'But Mr. Dean will want to know all the usual things, I expect, so are you going to make notes?'

'Oh! Oh yes, of course.' He spread a clean sheet of paper in front of him and held his pencil poised, looking at her hopefully.

'My full name is Caitlin Elizabeth O'Connor,' she told him, and watched him write it down in a neat square hand. She spelled out her first name for him and he nodded his thanks.

'That's very unusual,' he remarked. 'And very pretty.'

'It's a Gaelic name my mother found in a book,' Cadie confessed, 'but I could never pronounce it as a child, hence the diminutive.'

'That's pretty too,' he told her. 'I've never come across either before.'

'I always hated my name when I was at school,' Cadie confessed. 'It's one of those names that leaves one wide open to all sorts of awful nicknames.'

'I can well imagine,' he sympathized. He sat with his chin resting on one hand, his brown eyes watching her earnestly, then, as if he suddenly remembered he was failing in his task, he put pen to paper again. 'Your age, Miss O'Connor, if I may?'

'Twenty-three,' Cadie answered promptly. 'I was twenty-three last March.'

'Thank you.' He duly noted it, then turned his attention to her qualifications and her former employment, guided by Cadie herself. It was quite amusing, she thought, rather as if she was conducting her own interview.

'Now you ask me when I can start,' she told him with a smile. 'And I say next week if you want me to. My boss has agreed to allow me only a week's notice instead of a month, if I get the job.'

'Oh, good!' He made a note of it. 'Is there anything else I've forgotten?'

'I don't think so,' Cadie told him. 'Except to discover where I should be living if I come to Dorly Creek, and the answer is that Dottie's found me a nice little cottage not too far away, so she says, although I haven't seen it yet.'

'Oh, I know that much,' he said with a smile. 'I helped Dottie look for somewhere for you and we were very thrilled when Creek Cottage came vacant just right.'

'Oh, I see.' Dottie had forgotten to mention that little matter.

'I'm sure you'll like it,' he told her. 'And it's very convenient, just at the back of here actually.'

'Oh, marvellous,' Cadie laughed. 'I shall be able to indulge my laziness. Now all that remains is for Mr.

Dean to decide whether I've got the job or not.'

'I'm sure you will—' He stopped short, and before Cadie could turn, someone spoke behind her, the voice dismayingly familiar.

'Oh, it's you,' he said.

She had not even heard the door open behind her, but she turned in her chair, her eyes wide and dismayed when she met the amusement and hint of mockery in the face of the man she had met so disastrously yesterday.

He came further into the room, and Cadie was surprised to discover that he was even taller than she had realized. The light grey eyes held much the same expression she had met before through the window of her car, and invoked much the same reaction from her.

Her hands tightened over the top of her bag and she looked at him down her small, slightly tip-tilted nose. 'I suppose you're going to spoil everything for me by telling Mr. Dean what a fool you think I am,' she suggested, and he laughed.

'It's a temptation, I admit,' he confessed. 'I heard the voice from the other side of the door and I couldn't believe my ears. I just had to see if it was you.'

'Now you know,' Cadie said, 'what are you going to do?'

He shrugged, perching on the edge of the desk, his long legs stretched out in front of him, looking very much at ease. 'Oh, don't worry,' he told her. 'I won't do anything to stop you getting the job, and I don't believe you *are* a fool really. Just a day-dreamer, and that's one of the drawbacks of your sex, so I can't

19

blame you.' His gaze swept over her briefly but so meaningly that she coloured furiously and bit her lip hard. 'There are far more compensations than drawbacks, I think,' he added, and winked at Gordon Charles, who looked uneasy and embarrassed. 'Get her to sign on the dotted line, Gordon, before she changes her mind.'

'Rob—' Gordon Charles looked at him anxiously, while Cadie stared in surprise, her huge eyes blank with disbelief.

'You're – you're Robert Dean?'

He nodded, solemn-faced but with a wicked gleam in his eyes. 'Does it surprise you?' he asked, and Cadie nodded, her head spinning with the confusion of it. 'Why?'

'Because—' She realized suddenly that he was laughing at her and she stuck out her chin defiantly. 'Because Dottie described you as gorgeous,' she retorted rashly, 'and quite frankly I don't agree with her.'

'Oh, you don't?' He still sat there watching her, and he was still finding it more amusing than annoying. 'Well, she didn't do a very good job on your advance publicity either,' he said. 'She could have warned me to expect fireworks.' The grey gaze swept over her again and he laughed softly. 'I shall have to have words with Dottie, she's let me in for more than I bargained for.'

'I—'

He ignored her attempt to speak, and got to his feet. 'Let me see you here a week on Monday morning at nine o'clock,' he told her, and walked out of the room, leaving Cadie staring after him.

'I've a good mind not to take on the blessed job,' Cadie told Dottie some time later. 'Dottie, how could you be so wrong about anybody? He's awful! Conceited, arrogant, and — and supercilious!'

'Oh no, Cadie, he isn't, honestly!' Dottie looked at her anxiously. 'You won't turn it down, will you?'

Cadie battled with her pride for a few minutes, then she smiled ruefully. 'I suppose not,' she agreed at last. 'I'd be a fool not to take the opportunity while it's there, wouldn't I? After all, it's much better pay for one thing.' She smiled at Dottie's round, earnest face and hugged her impulsively. 'And you did go to a lot of trouble to get it for me too, didn't you?'

'It was rather a neat piece of Mata Hari type coaxing,' Dottie admitted with a gleeful chuckle, 'but it worked, and I know you won't regret coming, Cadie.'

'No, I suppose I won't in the long run,' Cadie agreed. 'It isn't as if Robert Dean lives there alone either, is it?' she added, and Dottie giggled.

'Gordon's rather a pet, isn't he?'

'He's very charming and polite,' Cadie agreed. 'Just about everything his stepbrother isn't, in fact.'

'Oh, but you've really misjudged poor Rob,' Dottie insisted. 'He's very nice, Cadie, and I know you'll enjoy working for him when you get used to his ways.'

'I hope so,' Cadie sighed.

'And you won't change your mind?' Cadie shook her head, and Dottie nodded satisfaction. 'Good, I'm glad. I know you won't regret it, love, honestly.'

CHAPTER TWO

IT was only a week later that Cadie moved into the little cottage at the rear of Dorly House and, to her surprise and delight, Gordon Charles arrived after a very short time to see her safely in, as he told her. He brought her a beautiful bouquet of pink roses and an invitation to have lunch with him.

She was obliged to refuse the latter, albeit regretfully, because she had already arranged to lunch with Dottie and Michael, but Gordon looked flatteringly disappointed at her refusal. 'Perhaps another time?' he suggested, and Cadie smiled.

'I'd love to,' she told him. 'Thank you, Mr. Charles.'

'I'd much rather you called me Gordon.' She met the gaze of his nice brown eyes and smiled. He was really very attractive and quite charming.

'Thank you, Gordon.'

'That's better!' The way he was smiling at her did not exactly fit in with the image she had had of him until now, but she could find nothing to object to.

'And you must call me Cadie,' she insisted, and he nodded.

'I hoped you'd say that.'

She looked round the small, sunny room and laughed, a little uneasy suddenly, although she could not have said why. 'I have quite a bit of straightening out to do yet,' she said. 'It's a good job I have most of the week-end.'

'Do you like your little house?'

She nodded. 'I love it,' she told him, and meant it. 'Especially the view of the creek from this window. It was so unexpected somehow, I thought Dorly House was right at the tip of the creek, I didn't realize it went this far round.'

'The creek itself doesn't,' Gordon explained. 'What you can see from here is a little tributary that runs off the creek itself, although you can see that if you look from one side of the window.'

'Whatever it is it makes a lovely view,' Cadie said, 'and I can't get over being so lucky as to find it empty at just the right time.'

'It was lucky,' he agreed. 'It's only a couple of weeks since the old couple who *were* here moved out. When I suggested you could have it and be handy for work, Rob was quite agreeable, and of course Dottie was delighted about it.'

Cadie looked at him for a moment, startled by his words. This was something Dottie had not seen fit to mention, probably deliberately. 'Do you mean – this cottage belongs to Mr. Dean?' she asked.

'Oh yes, didn't Dottie tell you? It came with the house when Rob bought it years ago, and the old folks were in it then. He didn't need it, so he just let them stay on as they were, then two weeks ago they decided to go and live with their son and his family, which was very fortuitous from your point of view.'

'Very.' She looked out at the miniature creek beyond

her window, shining in the sun. and lapping lazily at the narrow yellow edges of sand that bordered it. 'I didn't realize it was Mr. Dean's property, though.'

He seemed to sense her feelings in the matter and looked at her curiously, as if he thought she might change her mind about staying. 'It doesn't make any difference, does it, Cadie?'

She turned and smiled at him. 'No, of course not,' she denied. 'I'm going to love it here, just as Dottie does. It's so marvellously peaceful and pretty here, and I'm eternally grateful to you and Dottie for getting it for me.'

He looked relieved, she thought. 'Good, I'm glad you like it.'

'One thing puzzles me,' she said, remembering another point that until now had not bothered her too much. 'The rent is fantastically low compared to anything I've ever come across in town. Are rents lower here or am I being subsidized by the boss?' The idea of that did not please her at all, but she would be very reluctant to give up the cottage now, even for a principle.

'Neither,' Gordon hastened to assure her. 'Please don't think that and feel you have to protest. Rents here can be pretty high, but Rob simply hasn't done anything about putting it up since the old people left, that's all.'

'Oh, I see.'

'I know you're a very independent spirit,' he told her with a smile, 'but you have nothing to worry about on that score, Cadie.'

'Good.' She looked around the room again. 'Well, I'd better get started if I'm going to be straight by Monday. My own bits of furniture fit in very well with what's already here, don't they?'

'Very well,' he agreed, looking around. 'Are you thinking of changing it round?'

'Just a bit,' she said, and laughed at his expression of puzzled curiosity. 'It's something that women like doing,' she told him. 'It isn't your own house until you've arranged it to suit yourself.'

'Oh, I see. Can I stay and help you move things about?'

She shook her head. 'I'd rather you didn't,' she told him. 'I may have anything up to a dozen changes of mind about any one piece of furniture and you'd go crazy shifting it from one place to another. Much better if I do it myself, thank you, Gordon.'

'You're sure?'

'Quite sure, thank you. I suppose,' she added, 'Mr. Dean won't have any objection to my moving the furniture around?'

'Of course not. You're paying the rent, you do as you like here – short of knocking the walls down, of course.'

'I hadn't thought of *that*,' she told him. 'And I hope you speak with authority about me moving things. I've already started off on the wrong foot twice, I'd hate to make it a hat-trick.'

'Well, you won't, so don't worry about it.' He looked at her for a second as if he would say more, then shook his head and smiled. 'I'd better leave you to it, if you're sure I can't help.'

'I can manage quite well on my own, thank you.'

'That independent spirit again,' he smiled. 'Are you sure about lunch?'

'Quite sure, thank you, Gordon. I've promised Dottie.'

'O.K.' He left rather reluctantly, she thought, as she watched him drive away, and she wondered at the different effect he had on her in comparison to his stepbrother. She could become quite attracted to Gordon Charles with very little effort.

With a sigh she turned back into the cottage and set about rearranging some of the furniture to better suit her own taste, a task she had to admit she enjoyed.

She finished at last, everything to her satisfaction, and glanced at her watch. It was time she cleaned herself up and started out for Dottie's, if she was to arrive in time for lunch as she had promised. A glance in the mirror over the mantel made her smile ruefully at the sight she presented to herself.

Her hair, hastily tied back under a triangle of cotton that covered her head, and a large smear of combined dust and furniture polish, left behind by a careless hand, decorating her left cheek. Her cheeks were flushed with the exertion of moving furniture and to crown it all she had donned a large print apron loaned by her mother and which engulfed her completely from her waist to well below her knees.

No wonder then that she turned in dismay when she heard a car draw up outside and a second later someone rat-tatted sharply on the brass knocker. A swift glance out of the window revealed Robert Dean on the doorstep and she almost groaned audibly when she saw him.

There was no time to do anything about her appearance, however, and she merely wiped her dusty palms down the voluminous apron as she went to open the door.

'Hello.' He missed nothing of her dishevelment, of course, and his gaze came to rest on her flushed face, a brief smile playing havoc with her self-confidence.

'Hello.' She hesitated before standing back to admit him. 'You can come in if you don't mind the way I look. I was just going to change and clean up.'

'You look O.K. to me,' he assured her calmly. 'Domesticity suits you.'

She led the way into the transformed sitting-room and turned to look at him, waiting for his reaction, wondering indeed if he had ever seen it as it was before. She could not imagine that he was the type who went calling on his tenants very often.

'Is this a landlord's inspection?' she asked, her chin tilted defiantly, and he shook his head, smiling as he perched himself on the arm of a chair.

'Were you expecting one?' he countered, and went on before she could reply. 'I see you've been shifting things around already,' he added. 'Do you like the cottage?'

'Very much.' She felt oddly like a poor peasant beholden to a landlord for her home and, while the feeling rankled, she felt she should at least thank him for letting her have it. 'I – I'm grateful to you for letting me have it,' she told him.

'Oh, so someone told you, did they?' He cocked a quizzical brow at her and smiled. 'Gordon, I suspect.'

'He – he did tell me you owned it,' she admitted. 'I think Dottie might have told me it was yours.'

He laughed softly, one foot swinging as he studied her thoughtfully. 'I think Dottie knows you too well,' he told her. 'She probably knew you'd refuse to take it if you knew it was my property, especially once she knew how we'd met for the first time.'

'I'm not so stupid as to refuse a place just because I know it belongs to you,' she denied.

'But it's what you dislike most,' he insisted. 'Having to say thank you to me for it. Aren't I right?'

'I suspect you always are,' Cadie retorted, even more conscious of the dust smear on her cheek, and the huge enveloping apron. She missed the reassurance of her well-dressed, efficient secretarial image and wished he would go.

'Always right?' He laughed and shook his head. 'I wish I was.'

Cadie looked down at her grubby hands and kept her eyes on the tight little bundle her hankie made in the pocket of the apron. If only he would go and leave her to have her bath and change! If only she had the courage to tell him to go, but she was unsure just what rights he had as a landlord in a situation like this.

'If you – if you object to my turning the furniture around,' she told him, seeking another subject, 'I can always move it back where it was.'

He looked as if he had forgotten all about the furniture. 'You do as you like with it,' he told her. 'It's a typical feminine pastime, isn't it? Shifting the furniture about.'

'Is it?'

She had told Gordon so herself, but she was not ready to admit as much to him when he would use it against her for sure. He sat with one leg crossed over the other, elegant and so completely self-assured that she would have loved to have tipped the chair and sent him sprawling.

'I'd have been better pleased, however,' he went on unaware of her plans for him, 'if you'd asked Gordon while he was here to move it for you. This old stuff's pretty heavy and you're small enough to blow over with a good puff.'

Such consideration for her welfare was totally unexpected and Cadie felt a momentary flicker of conscience for having been so ungracious. 'Oh, I managed all right,' she told him, a hint of smile in her blue eyes which he responded to swiftly.

'So I see,' he said, 'but I don't want you laid up with a sprained wrist or whatever before you've been here five minutes. I've got a lot of work for you to do.'

'Oh, I see.' She hastily banished the smile and pulled the cotton scarf from her head in a gesture of annoyance for her own gullibility. 'Well, you needn't worry about it – I'm all in one piece.'

That light grey, arrogant gaze swept over her again from top to toe and he smiled meaningly. 'So you are,' he said softly. 'And a very nice piece too.'

'Mr. Dean—'

'Are you always this spiky?' he asked, watching her colour rise again.

'Spiky?' She held her head back and knew he was laughing to himself, and the knowledge infuriated her.

'Prickly. Ready to bite my head off at the drop of a hat. Do you always treat men like this, or am I singled out for special attention?'

'You just happen to bring the worst out in me,' Cadie retorted, stung to indiscretion, and he looked at her steadily for a moment in silence.

'Gordon seems to have hit on the right formula,' he said at last. 'I must ask him how he managed it.'

'By not criticizing my driving for a start,' Cadie informed him, and he laughed, shaking his head.

'I knew it!' he declared, so satisfied he was right. 'You really took that to heart, didn't you?'

'Of course I did!' She stuck out her chin, the light of battle in her blue eyes, making them dark and angry. 'I detest men who make disparaging remarks about women drivers with no foundation for them except sheer, unadulterated prejudice.'

He appeared to be regarding her solemnly enough, but his eyes betrayed the amusement he felt at her protest, and she resented it bitterly. 'I'll bet you go protesting with your little banner when you're in London, don't you?' he asked, and Cadie curled her hands into fists. If anyone could drive her into being an out-and-out feminist it was this man.

'No, I do not,' she said.

'Well, I hope you won't try it here,' he told her, ignoring her denial. 'It wouldn't go down at all well, and the female population of Dorly Creek are very unlikely to join you in making lingerie bonfires on the quay.'

'Oh, you—!'

'I'm just warning you,' he went on with a grin that aroused all sorts of violent instincts in her.

'I can't *think*,' she declared darkly, 'why Dottie finds you so – so—'

'Irresistible?' he suggested softly, and laughed at her black frown.

'Gorgeous is her word,' Cadie retorted, 'and I don't agree with either.'

'So you said before.' He was still laughing at her and there was something distinctly disturbing about the easy posture of his lean length on the chair arm, and the brown face with its thatch of blond hair. Something she recognized and hastily dismissed. Dottie could rave about him as much as she liked, she had no intention of being blinded by mere animal attraction. 'Dottie's quite a different cup of tea from you,' he informed her. 'She's a willing victim of masculine charm, you're the sort who demands a fighting conquest, Cadie.'

The easy use of her christian name took her by surprise for a moment, then she frowned over it. 'Don't—' she began, but got no further.

'Now you're going to object to me calling you Cadie,' he guessed, unperturbed. 'Well, you can please yourself whether it's Cadie or Caitlin, but I flatly refuse to call you Miss O'Connor.'

31

'I see. Whether I like it or not?'

He nodded. 'Whether you like it or not,' he echoed. 'I've never been on such formal terms with my secretaries, and I'm not going to start now.'

'And I imagine there have been quite a few of them,' Cadie suggested sweetly.

He looked at her steadily for a moment, then shook his head. 'No, there hasn't,' he denied. 'Dottie was only my second, and I was very sorry to lose her.'

'I – I'm sorry.' She wasn't quite sure just why she was apologizing suddenly, and he said nothing for a while, then he cupped her chin in his hand and raised her dust-streaked face to look at him, his grey eyes serious for the first time.

'Don't make me sorry I took Dottie's word about you,' he said quietly. 'I don't think you can be as acid as you appear and still be a friend of Dottie's.' He lifted her chin sharply and made her look at him. 'Are you?' he demanded.

Cadie put up a hand to ease the hold on her, and unexpectedly, he released her chin and captured her hand instead, studying the slim fingers that instinctively curled over his. 'I'm not – not acid, as you call it,' she denied. 'I'm – I'm just a perfectly ordinary woman, as good a secretary as most, and better than some.'

'Oh no,' he said softly. 'Not ordinary, I won't have that. You're lovely, even beautiful, which is something Dottie should have warned me about too, and I hope you're as efficient as Dottie says you are.'

'I – I am efficient.' She tried to free her hand, but he

had no intention at the moment of allowing her to, and he was as strong as she would have expected him to be.

'Good. Because if you're not I shall have to give you the sack, and I'm sure Gordon would hate me if I did that.'

'But there's—'

'He's quite besotted with you, did you know that?' he asked casually, ignoring her attempt to protest, and Cadie bit her lip.

'That's ridiculous,' she objected firmly. 'I've only seen Mr. Charles twice.'

'That's enough for Gordon,' he informed her with a smile for his stepbrother's weakness. 'He's been madly in love with every pretty girl he's ever met, and you're the prettiest one yet.'

'Mr. Dean! Will you please let go my hand?'

'Mmm.' He brushed his lips briefly against her fingers before releasing them, watching her steadily to see what she would do next.

The mention of Gordon's past affairs had, she felt, been made with the specific intention of warning her not to take his stepbrother seriously, and she wondered why he had bothered. Even if it was true, for Gordon did not give the impression that he would take anything lightly, such behaviour was surely more in keeping with Robert Dean's nature.

She had seldom felt at such a loss. Obviously from his expression he expected some sort of reaction from her, and she sought for words that would make light of the suggestion. 'You have no need to worry about anything between Gordon and me,' she told him, finding words at last. 'It's rather early in the day for there to be anything to worry *about*.'

'Hmm.' He held her gaze until she could stand it no longer and walked across to the window, seeking a change of subject. Something less personal and embarrassing than Gordon Charles' finding her attractive.

She stood with her back to him, looking out at the little creek and its yellow sandy shore, with a view of the houses on the other side of the water. If only she could come to terms with the man who watched her so intently, she would enjoy being here, but she wondered if she ever could. He always, without fail, seemed to rouse her to some kind of resentment and anger and it worried her not a little.

She heard him move and he came and stood just behind her, speaking over her shoulder. 'You're not having second thoughts about coming to work for me, are you?' he asked quietly, and Cadie half turned her head to look at him.

'No,' she said,'I don't think so.'

'I'm sure you'll like it here, Dottie loves it.'

'I know.' She smiled at Dottie's enthusiasm. 'You — you don't regret her having talked you into taking me on in her place, do you?' she asked impulsively.

The light grey eyes mocked her for a moment before becoming serious again. 'I'll let you know the answer to that next week this time,' he told her.

Breakfast on Monday morning consisted of nothing more than two hastily gulped cups of coffee, because

Cadie found herself unusually anxious, far too much so to eat anything. She checked her appearance for the hundredth time and brushed the shiny black length of her hair yet again. It was quite ridiculous to feel so nervous at the prospect of a new job, and she shook herself determinedly as she looked again in the long mirror.

The white shirtwaister she wore showed off her colouring well, and low-heeled navy pumps deprived her of height but added to an overall, delightfully petite look. It was such a short distance to the house that she could do no other than walk, and she set off, rather early, down the narrow lane behind Dorly House, enjoying the warmth of the sun and a tempering breeze blowing in off the sea.

There appeared to be no one about as she walked up the steps to the front door, but it was ajar again as it had been on her first visit. She put a hand to the bell, peering into the dimness of the hall, and wondering if the Mrs. Calthrop that Gordon had alluded to ever answered the door, for no one came in answer to her ring.

She was about to venture into the hall when Robert Dean appeared and looked across at her with raised brows, signalling to her with an impatient hand. 'Come on in,' he told her. 'Don't stand around out there.'

Cadie did as she was bid and he waited for her in the doorway, watching her in such a way that she knew the colour rose to her cheeks, and as she came closer he smiled.

'Good morning, Mr. Dean.' She made her greeting

formal and polite, determined to start off right today.

'You're a sight to gladden the eyes on a Monday morning,' he informed her, leading the way into the office she had seen before. 'And you're early too, aren't you?'

'A bit, I suppose,' Cadie allowed. 'Does it matter?'

'Matter?' He cocked a quizzical brow at her and she knew without doubt that he was laughing at her formality. 'Of course it doesn't matter if you're early, I shall only blow your head off if you're late.'

'I'm never late.'

'Oh, I see.' He opened desk drawers to show her how much room she had for her things and laughed softly as he stood over her. 'A paragon of virtue,' he mocked.

'Oh, please!' The plea was heartfelt as she saw her good intentions coming to nothing if he persisted in teasing her.

'Something wrong?' he asked, perching himself on the edge of her desk.

'No. No, not if you don't keep trying to take a rise out of me. I want to – I want to like this job, and I think I could if you'd stop always trying to make me look small.'

He stood up straight for a second, his superior height towering over her. 'You *are* small,' he told her. 'I don't have anything to do with it.'

'Yes, you *do*,' Cadie insisted, putting away her handbag and setting the desk to suit her own way of working. 'You keep making me lose my temper with you and I'm always sorry afterwards.'

'Are you?' He looked down at her, a gentle, half teasing look in his eyes and he was smiling too. 'Shall I not tease you, then, Cadie? Is that what you want?'

She looked up at him with a small frown. 'I – I don't mean to sound like a prig,' she told him. 'I don't really mind being teased, it's just that—'

'I always say the wrong thing,' he guessed, and she hastily lowered her eyes. 'All right, Cadie.' He got up from her desk and stood looking at her for a moment or two. 'I'll remember, although it won't be easy. I used to tease the life out of Dottie and she never turned a hair.'

'Dottie wouldn't,' she admitted ruefully. 'She hasn't such a low flashpoint as I have.'

'Truce?' He proffered a hand, and she put her own into it, his fingers gently squeezing hers.

'Truce,' she agreed.

They worked in silence for a couple of hours and Cadie was surprised to find how quickly the time had gone. It was already eleven o'clock when the door opened suddenly after a brief preliminary knock, and Gordon appeared. He looked across at her and smiled before speaking to his stepbrother.

'It's eleven,' he told him. 'Are you and Cadie coming out for coffee?'

'No.'

The brief negative startled her somewhat and she was to be given no opportunity to answer for herself, apparently, so she made a wry face at Gordon. 'Can't Cadie come and have hers?' he asked.

Robert looked up and his eyes flicked only briefly in Cadie's direction before he looked at Gordon. 'I'm afraid not,' he told him. 'We're getting on far too well to leave it for some social backchat session now.'

'Lida's here,' Gordon offered by way of persuasion, but Robert did not even look up again.

'I don't care if the King of Siam's here,' he replied shortly. 'I'm busy, get Mrs. Calthrop to bring us some coffee, will you?'

Gordon shrugged resignedly. 'O.K.,' he agreed. 'If that's the way you want it.'

'That's the way I want it.'

'What shall I tell Lida?'

Robert looked up again, his brows raised. 'Damn it, Gordon, you know what to tell her. Tell her I'm busy. Lida knows better by now than to throw a temperament when I'm working.'

'O.K.' he gave a last rueful glance at Cadie and went out again.

Cadie's brain was rapidly going through all the names she could remember that Dottie had listed as Robert's women friends. They were many and varied, but mostly well known in one field or another, and she thought the Lida in question must be an abbreviation of Mellida Dawson – the latest and most serious, according to Dottie, in a long line of passing fancies.

Cadie had seen many photographs of Mellida Dawson; she was one of the most photographed actresses in the business and supposedly able to name her own price for any part she cared to play. She had appeared in several plays written by Robert Dean and

Cadie was only surprised to hear her dismissed in such cavalier fashion by her employer. It seemed his arrogance was not confined to his treatment of Cadie alone.

'Are you peeved because I stopped your coffee break?' he asked, so suddenly that Cadie hastily blinked herself back to reality, unsure if she had heard him aright.

'Sorry?'

'I thought you were on your high horse again,' he told her, 'because you couldn't go with Gordon and have your coffee.'

'Well, I'm not.'

'Then I'm sorry I spoke.'

'Why on earth should I mind if I don't go out and have my coffee?' she asked. 'It's not usual.'

'It is here, when there's time,' he told her.

'That's reasonable, when there's time.'

'Then you're not mad because I've deprived you of Gordon's devoted company?'

Cadie looked across at him, her eyes dark with warning. 'I thought you were going to give up trying to make me angry,' she said, and he raised both hands defensively.

'So I did, I'd forgotten.'

'You have no reason to keep making suggestions that Gordon and I are – are, well anything at all.'

'No?'

'No,' Cadie echoed firmly.

'Then I'm sorry. O.K.?'

'O.K.' She was obliged to smile at the look he wore which she supposed was the nearest he ever got to looking contrite, and he was laughing when the door opened again, this time to admit the sleek and familiar good looks of Mellida Dawson.

She looked older somehow than Cadie expected her to, although the short skirt and fitted sweater she wore gave her a lean, almost boyish look. Blonde hair, shoulder-length, swung loose about her face as she put her head on one side to judge Robert's reaction to her appearance.

'I've brought your coffee,' she informed him, taking Cadie to be part of the office furnishings, apparently, since she did not even look at her. 'Aren't I kind, after the way you refused to come and see me?'

'I'm busy, Lida.' He nevertheless leaned back in his chair for a moment, his smile resigned. 'You never take no for an answer, do you?'

'Not when there's a chance you'll change your mind,' the actress admitted, and sat on the edge of his desk, leaning forward to kiss his mouth; a gesture he appeared to take no interest in.

'I told you I was busy,' he said. 'Now get lost, Lida, before I lose my temper and throw you out.'

'You wouldn't, darling, would you?'

'I would,' Robert assured her, making no move to carry out the threat.

The actress's sharp blue eyes looked across at Cadie at last and she raised her pencilled brows as if she had only now noticed the change. 'Oh, I see you've had a change of female. What happened to the other one?'

'Dottie is expecting,' he informed her, 'so she found me Cadie to take her place.'

'Cadie?'

'Caitlin, to be precise,' he said. 'Caitlin O'Connor.'

'Good God, what a name!'

Cadie tried not to clench her hands, but it was difficult to face the woman and not let her know that she found her rudeness intolerable. 'It's rather in the same stable as yours I would have said, Lida,' he told her calmly, ignoring the annoyed pout she gave. 'Cadie, this is Mellida Dawson, in case you hadn't already recognized her.'

Cadie met the clear, sharp blue eyes warily. It was not difficult to recognize Mellida Dawson as one of those women who rarely get along with her own sex, and she would make a formidable enemy if she did not take kindly to her.

'Miss Dawson.' The blonde head merely nodded acknowledgement, then she turned to Robert again, deciding to ignore her.

'Rob darling,' she said, in a pseudo little-girl voice, *why* don't you leave that just for a few minutes and come and have coffee with me?'

'Because I don't have the time,' he told her bluntly. 'Thanks for bringing in our coffee, Lida. Now go away like a good girl while we get back to work.'

She resented being sent packing, Cadie thought, but she made surprisingly little fuss about going and merely pouted her disappointment as she slid off his desk.

'One of these days,' she told him, 'I'll *really* go away for good, Robert, and then see how you get on.'

'I'll survive,' he informed her cheerfully, and laughed when she slammed the door behind her. 'Come and pour out our coffee, will you, Cadie?'

CHAPTER THREE

'SHE was livid,' Cadie said, regaling Dottie with the news of Mellida Dawson's dismissal, later that evening. 'And I can't really blame her either.'

'Oh, she'll get over it,' Dottie said blithely, and sounding very much like her former employer. 'That sort thrive on take-it-or-leave-it treatment, and Rob knows it.'

'He's quite the most conceited man *I've* ever met,' Cadie declared. 'I've never seen anyone like him.'

Dottie giggled. 'Oh, he's a rare one, is our Robert,' she said. 'A monster in a way, but lovely with it.'

'The first part I agree with,' Cadie retorted. 'Not the second. I could cheerfully throw the typewriter at him at times.'

'Oh, you couldn't!'

'I could,' Cadie insisted, forgetting for the moment the truce they had. 'I probably will too before the week's out.'

'I never had *that* sort of urge when I was with him,' Dottie said, and Cadie looked at her curiously, remembering Robert Dean's opinion of her as a willing victim of male charm. Cadie could not help wondering how true it was. Certainly she had met and married Michael in a very short time, but there was nothing of the fatal charmer about Michael. He was very nice and very ordinary, but he had swept Dottie off her feet with no trouble at all, so perhaps Robert Dean was right after all. About Dottie, at least, not about herself.

It was Cadie's first Saturday night in Dorly Creek, and Gordon had arranged to come for her at seven o'clock. 'We'll have dinner first, then either gamble or dance, or perhaps even both,' he told her when he first mentioned it. 'You'll like Dorfleet, Cadie, and there's a very good restaurant to the casino.'

Dorfleet was nearly three miles further round the coast than Dorly Creek, and vastly different in character. It was much bigger for one thing, and had all the modern amenities for enjoying oneself, including a gambling club. It was the latter idea that rather intrigued Cadie who, although she had lived for years in London, had never ventured into a gambling club.

She had consulted Dottie on what she should wear and they had decided that a short, silver grey silk was most suitable. It was quite the most luxurious dress Cadie had ever possessed, and she had had it made up from a length of pure silk that her father had brought back from the East for her. Made after the style of a cheongsam, it set off her black-haired beauty to perfection, and in some strange way, made her eyes look even more blue.

She wondered if Gordon would approve of its rather close fit, but she need not have worried, for, when she answered the door to him, he stood back for a moment, gazing at her in speechless amazement.

'Will I do?' she asked, twirling round for his inspection, and he nodded.

'You look beautiful,' he told her. 'Absolutely beautiful, Cadie. I'd never have believed that you could look even lovelier, but you do.'

'Thank you.' She held his gaze and laughed softly, feeling very lighthearted at the prospect of her evening out.

'You're the loveliest girl I've ever known,' he told her. 'And in that dress—'

'It's not too—'

'It's perfect,' he assured her. 'You look stunning enough to take everybody's breath away.'

He saw her into his car, a rather less ostentatious model than the one his stepbrother drove, but nevertheless sleek and shiny enough to make her feel very grand and pampered as she sat beside him. It was a warm night and she had no coat, just a small evening purse and a long, floaty scarf to cover her head in the open car.

They drove along the coast road in brilliant moonlight and Cadie thought how wonderful it all looked. The waves breaking, white-ruffled on the glistening sand, and the silvery endlessness of the sea beyond the trees that lined the road. It was all very romantic and rather exciting, and almost instinctively she glanced at her companion.

He looked darker in the moonlight and better-looking too, although he was always good-looking in a rather old-fashioned way. Much less startling in colouring than his stepbrother, he looked more romantic and very attractive in this setting.

As if he sensed her scrutiny at last, he turned his

45

head and smiled at her. 'We can have a mild flutter after dinner if you'd like to,' he suggested. 'There's most of the usual games at the casino, and I've a feeling you might bring me luck.'

'I hope so,' she said. 'I've never been to a gambling club before, but I'd love to, and see how I like it.'

'You've nothing against gambling?'

She shook her head. 'No, nothing at all,' she replied. 'Kept within the bounds of reason.' She looked at him curiously. 'Do you often come?'

'Sometimes,' he said. 'Not so often really, it can be expensive if your luck goes against you.'

'Mmm, I suppose it can.'

'Incidentally,' he added, with a swift glance at her, 'we might bump into Rob tonight. He told me just before lunch that he was coming here tonight.' He laughed shortly. 'Doing his own research for a change because it suits him to.'

'Oh yes, the play we're working on is concerned with a gambling club.'

'That's right. He always likes to soak up a certain amount of atmosphere himself, even though I do most of the actual research for him.'

Cadie was very tempted to ask if he was coming alone, but she did not see how she could do so without causing some speculation as to her reason for asking. The question was answered, however, by Gordon volunteering the information.

'His problem, of course,' he told her with a wry smile, 'is getting here alone. He likes to be on his own when he's more or less working and Lida isn't very easy to dissuade.'

'Oh, I see.'

Again she was tempted to ask if there was anything very serious between Robert and Mellida Dawson, but she resisted for the same reason, but this time there was no answer forthcoming.

The restaurant was, as he had promised, excellent, and she enjoyed her first meal out for some time. Gordon was good company and attentive enough to make her feel very good. His attention combined with the effect of the silk dress on her morale was electric and she had seldom felt brighter or more excited as they made their way to the gambling rooms.

Gordon glanced down at her briefly, squeezing her arm and smiling down at her. 'I'm sure you'll be lucky for me,' he told her. 'You look like a beautiful goddess of good fortune.'

'I hope I will be.' She laughed, but she was feeling tense with anticipation as they walked into the lushly carpeted gambling rooms. The serious business of winning and losing gave an air of stimulation to the whole place and it immediately affected her. Tonight, she thought, was going to be different.

There was quite a crowd at almost every table and for a moment they stood, waiting for someone to go, or just watching others play. It was while they stood with the people watching the roulette that she spotted Robert.

He was difficult to miss, even in a crowd, with that blond hair looking almost silver in the overhead light, and the tanned face dark above a white shirt. When she noticed him first he wore a slight frown as if things were not going well for him, then he glanced up and saw her, and smiled.

He pushed forward a few of the counters he had in front of him and murmured a number she could not hear, then he raised a hand and signalled her to come over to him. Cadie glanced at Gordon inquiringly and saw the frown that greeted the somewhat imperious gesture.

'Shall we go over?' she asked, and he did not answer at once but looked as if he would like to say no.

'If you want to,' he said at last, and held on tightly to her arm as they made their way round the edge of the crowd to where Robert sat.

Robert's gesture must have been witnessed and understood by the people nearest to him, for they made a way through for Cadie and Gordon when they arrived, and Robert immediately reached out for Cadie's hand. 'There you are,' he said by way of a greeting. 'You've turned my luck!'

The croupier was indeed pushing a pile of counters across the table to him, and Cadie's heart gave a flick of excitement when she met his eyes. Gordon looked far less pleased and held on to her arm determinedly.

'The idea was that Cadie should bring *me* luck,' he told Robert, and his stepbrother turned a quizzical smile on him, one brow raised.

'Don't spoil it for me now,' he said. 'I've had rotten luck all evening until I saw Cadie, and now I've won. You leave her with me, Gordon, and maybe I'll get some of my losses back.'

'I'll do no such thing,' Gordon declared firmly. 'You find your own good luck token, Rob, and let go of mine. Cadie's coming with me.'

Distracted for a moment while he placed another bet, Robert still held on to her hand, and she felt rather like a prize being fought over by the two of them, while a few curious and knowing smiles were exchanged by the people nearby.

'Cadie!'

Gordon tugged at her arm, but with Robert's hand still holding on tight to hers she could not move and it looked as if he was not prepared to let her go. She looked down at him, his mouth crooked into a half smile, the light grey eyes speculative as he watched her face to see what she would do.

'Are you going to desert me after just one throw?' he asked softly, and Cadie hastily lowered her eyes to avoid the expression she saw in his.

'I think you can manage without my help, Mr. Dean,' she said, sounding dismayingly breathless. 'And I *did* come with Gordon.'

Another pile of chips slid in front of Robert and he glanced down at them and then at Cadie again. 'You see,' he said. 'You *are* bringing me luck.'

'But—'

The hand holding hers squeezed her fingers in a shameless effort to persuade her by fair means or foul, and she knew even before he spoke that she would do as he asked, no matter what Gordon said about it.

'Just once more,' he begged, his voice so soft that only she heard the words.

She nodded, glancing immediately at Gordon, her eyes asking for understanding, but he frowned blackly and let go his hold on her arm. Robert, in one sweeping gesture of bravado, pushed the whole pile of counters in front of him across to the croupier and murmured a number, and there was a soft murmur of anticipation from those nearest as they watched the wheel start to spin.

Cadie held her breath, hardly daring to look, and even Gordon leaned forward to watch the whirling ball as it bounced around the numbered wheel. It stopped at last and a sigh of sound went up from the watchers as the winning number was called out.

'You see!' Robert raised her fingers to his lips, a gleam of triumph in his eyes as he gathered in his winnings. 'Now I'll give up for tonight if you're going to leave me.'

'I'm with Gordon,' she said, and looked at him with a wide-eyed, puzzled look before she turned away. 'I – I couldn't really have turned your luck, could I?' she asked, and Robert laughed.

'You did,' he told her. 'Now you'd better see if you can do as much for Gordon.'

Gordon took her arm again, urging her along, anywhere as long as it was away from his stepbrother. He looked more angry than she would have thought possible and, instinctively, she put her own hand on the one that held her arm so tightly, and looked up at him. 'I'm sorry, Gordon.'

For a moment he kept his face set sternly to the front, then he turned and looked down at her and his expression changed to a wry smile. 'No, *I'm* sorry,' he told her. 'I shouldn't have made so much of what was, after all, nothing but a bit of rather childish superstition.'

'Surely Rob – your stepbrother didn't believe I brought him luck, did he?' she asked.

'Obviously he did.'

'But I'd have thought he was – well, much too practical to believe in things like that.'

'He's a writer, isn't he?' Gordon asked, as if that explained all. 'They're mostly a superstitious lot.'

'Are they?'

'Haven't you seen Rob's mascot?' he asked, and she knew from the way he smiled that his stepbrother kept the secret of his mascot well hidden.

'No,' she shook her head, feeling a little uneasy about being let into a confidence she felt Robert would not have wanted her to know.

'If you look in the top drawer of his desk,' Gordon told her with a smile, 'you'll find a small, grubby white bear. He's had it ever since he had his first play accepted, nearly nine years ago and he won't start without it. He's as superstitious as any old witch woman.'

'Gordon, I don't think you should be telling me this.' She frowned, feeling rather as if she was prying, although the confidence was none of her choosing. 'If Robert has a – a feeling that the mascot brings him luck, then I suppose it's his affair.'

'But it's a bit unexpected, you must agree,' Gordon insisted. 'You said yourself you would have thought he was much too practical for such things.'

'I know, but—'

'You don't know him very well yet,' Gordon told her. 'When you do you'll find he's a lot of things you don't expect.'

'Most people are when you know them better,' Cadie replied, and he looked at her sharply.

'Me too?' he asked, and she nodded after a second's hesitation.

'You too,' she admitted.

It was rather late when Gordon took her home and Cadie, after the initial disagreement about Robert, had enjoyed her evening with him. He was good company and an excellent dancer, and they had danced for several hours after they left the gambling club.

As they drove back along the coast road she began to remember the first part of the evening and the way Robert's luck had changed, wondering if he had returned home after he left the roulette table. She had not realized until this evening that Gordon was jealous of him. Not only of his professional success, but of his effect on women too.

It was possible that she had been a little too impulsive in allowing herself to be persuaded by Robert into staying on, when she was with Gordon, but she had always been impulsive and there had been no other reason behind her staying. She had been curious to see if he would win a third time in a row, that was all, no matter what Gordon thought.

'Cadie!'

She glanced at Gordon, startled for a moment. 'I'm – I'm sorry, Gordon, did you say something?'

He smiled wryly over his shoulder at her. 'It wouldn't have been much use if I had, would it?' he said. 'You weren't with me, were you?'

'I was in something of a trance,' she confessed.

'Something on your mind?'

She smiled and shook her head. 'Nothing serious – I was just thinking, that's all.'

'Something nice?'

She was reluctant to commit herself on that point, so she merely laughed and shrugged her shoulders. 'Something quite ordinary,' she told him.

'It's a lovely night,' he said, looking at the moonlit sea through the bordering trees. 'You should be having nice, romantic thoughts on a night like this.'

'I should, shouldn't I?' She leaned back her head against the seat and looked up at the clear, starry sky. 'It *is* a lovely night, as you say.'

'Can I take you out again tomorrow?'

She turned her head to look at him from under half closed lids. 'That would be very nice,' she said. 'I'm having lunch with Dottie, but after that I'm not doing anything very special.'

'Then shall I pick you up at Dottie's, about three?'

'Lovely!'

'We could go for a drive out to Dorly Point and have a picnic tea,' he suggested.

'It sounds wonderful.'

'Then it's a date. I'll pick you up at Dottie's and

we'll have a picnic.'

'I haven't been on a picnic since I was a little girl,' Cadie told him. 'It's a lovely idea.'

'I'm glad you approve.' He turned briefly and smiled at her, and Cadie's heart did a hasty skip. It would be all too easy to fall in love with Gordon, if she wasn't very careful.

He was very reluctant to go, even when he had seen her right to her door, and Cadie smiled to herself as she opened her front door. 'Good night, Gordon, I've had a lovely time.'

'I'm glad.' She reached inside the door then and switched on the light and he blinked for a moment at the unexpectedness of it. 'Cadie!' His hands held her firmly by the tops of her arms and he brought his face down close to hers. 'Don't go in yet.'

'It's late,' she reminded him, and he shook his head.

'It's Sunday tomorrow, you don't have to wake up early.'

'Oh, but I do,' she told him lightly. 'I have my household chores to do before I go to Dottie's. I can't laze in too long.'

His hands tightened and he shook his head again. 'A girl like you shouldn't have to do chores,' he told her, and Cadie laughed.

'A girl like me *has* to do chores,' she assured him. 'A house won't clean itself, however small it is.'

'I know that, but – oh, you know what I mean, Cadie. It's a lovely moonlight night, you look absolutely de-lectable in that dress and all you can talk about is doing housework! I can think of much better things to say and do.' He pulled her close in his arms suddenly and sought her mouth, his own urgent and rather rough, so that she moved uneasily and broke his hold on her.

'Gordon!'

'Oh, Cadie, you're so lovely I could eat you!'

'You're hurting my arms!'

'I'm sorry, darling.' The endearment came easily and she held her breath for a moment as he hugged her close. 'I shall fall in love with you, I know I shall. I'm more than half-way there already.'

'Gordon!' She pushed him away, gently because she did not want to hurt his feelings. He seemed rather vulnerable at the moment and she would hate to say the wrong thing. 'You've only known me a week.'

'I don't care how long it is,' he averred. 'I'm falling in love with you.'

Cadie was trying not to remember that Robert Dean had said Gordon fell in love with every pretty girl he ever met, but she could not dismiss the idea. In his way perhaps Gordon was as impulsive as she was herself.

She ran one finger round the shape of his lapel and looked at her finger as it moved. 'I'm sure you can't be,' she said cautiously. 'Not really in love, I mean, that's something that takes quite a long time, Gordon.'

'Not always,' he argued. 'What about love at first sight?'

She shook her head, keeping her eyes lowered, because he really looked very attractive and romantic in the half light and she was feeling just a bit lightheaded. 'I'm not sure there is such a thing,' she told him. 'How can you love anyone if you don't know them? It's not very logical, is it?'

'Logical!' He put his hands either side of her head, resting them on the wall of the minute porch over her front door, his breath warm on her cheeks when he spoke. 'What on earth had logic to do with love?'

'Well – nothing, I suppose.' She looked at him briefly, but found the expression in his eyes too disturbing and hastily lowered her own again. 'But you mustn't be in love with me yet, Gordon, it's too soon.'

'Why?'

'Why?' She stirred uneasily, feeling herself weakening. 'It – it just is, that's all.'

'Don't you think I'm capable of loving you?'

'Yes, yes, of course.' She tried not to look at him, but it was difficult when he was standing so close, and her heart was hammering mercilessly against her ribs. 'But–'

'Hmm?'

'Oh – oh, I don't know!'

'Of course you don't.' He lifed her chin with one hand and looked down at her, his eyes almost black in the dim lighting. 'You were going to say something,' he guessed, 'then you changed your mind.'

'No. No, I wasn't.'

He still held her chin and his gaze was a little disconcerting. 'Cadie – what's Rob been saying to you about me?'

'Rob?' She felt the uneasy skip her heart gave and eased her chin from his hand.

56

'Yes, Rob. Has he been telling tales about me?'

'Of course not!' She hoped she sounded convincing, but Gordon was not to be put off.

'Has he been telling you about – well, about other girls I've been out with?' he asked, and Cadie did not answer. Gordon sighed, one finger caressing gently against her cheek. 'Well, he's right in a way,' he allowed. 'He hasn't got a monopoly on female company, but he's obviously been trying to scuttle my chances with you, and for that I could hit him.'

'Oh, Gordon, no!'

'Yes, I could,' he insisted. 'Why the devil can't he leave my affairs to me and get on with his own? What did he tell you anyway?'

'Nothing much—'

'I'd like to know.'

Cadie sighed. 'He – he merely said that you fall in love too easily.'

'And you believe him?'

She raised her eyes and looked at him steadily. 'I – I think I have to, Gordon, in a way. You've only known me a little over a week and you're already saying you're in love with me, and you can't possibly be.'

'Cadie!'

'You can't, Gordon, you know you can't.'

He was silent for a second or two, then he shrugged and bent his head to kiss her lightly on her mouth. 'O.K.,' he said. 'If you won't believe me, you won't, but that doesn't mean to say I shan't prove you wrong.'

'You're not angry because I told you?'

He kissed her again. 'I couldn't be angry with you,' he told her. 'But I'm livid with Rob.'

'Oh dear, you won't tell him, will you?'

He looked down at her quizzically. 'I might – why?'

'I – I wouldn't like him to think I've been carrying tales. Please, Gordon, don't say anything to him about it.'

'Does it matter that much what Rob thinks of you?' he asked, and Cadie shook her head, her eyes downcast again. 'Does it, Cadie?' He lifted her chin again and made her look at him. '*You're* not going weak at the knees for him too, are you?' he demanded.

'Certainly not!'

He nodded, but she was not at all sure that he was convinced and she wondered if he always suspected his stepbrother of trying to spoil his chances. 'I'm not going to change my mind about you, you know,' he told her, and she had to smile at the determination on his good-looking face as he looked down at her.

'As long as you don't change your mind about taking me on that picnic tomorrow,' she told him. 'I'm looking forward to it enormously.'

'I won't change my mind.' He kissed her again, long and earnestly as if he was trying to convince her of his seriousness. 'I'll see you tomorrow,' he said.

CHAPTER FOUR

CADIE was up quite early next morning, despite her late night, and she set about her housework as soon as she had finished breakfast. Not that there was very much to do with only herself living in the cottage, but she felt obliged to keep it spick and span in case of another unexpected visit from her landlord.

She left the kitchen until last, and took the opportunity, while she was dusting, of putting some of the things she was never likely to use up on to the top shelves of the old-fashioned dresser, out of the way.

It was a solid piece of furniture, and reached right up to the ceiling, with cupboards in the lower half and open shelves above the flat working surface. A pair of old steps, unearthed from the cellar, provided a means of access to the upper shelves, and she climbed, somewhat cautiously, from the top rung of the steps on to the flat working surface of the dresser.

An enormous, family-sized casserole and assorted other pots and pans she was never likely to have use for were stowed away neatly, and she was feeling rather pleased with her efforts when the front door knocker rat-tatted urgently for attention.

She frowned her annoyance at being interrupted, especially on a Sunday morning and definitely not looking her best. She wondered briefly if she could get away with simply staying where she was and hoping whoever it was would go away again. Curiosity, however, got the better of her and she also thought it could possibly be Gordon with a change of plans for the afternoon, so she sighed deeply and turned to reach for the steps again.

A clumsy move defeated her, however, and the flimsy erection collapsed before she could even put a foot on it, leaving her stranded on the top of the dresser with the floor looking an awfully long way away.

The clatter of the collapsing steps would surely have betrayed the fact that she was home, and by now her visitor must be growing impatient. Also, she realized, she would need assistance getting down from her perch. As the doors were open between the rooms it was possible that whoever it was would hear her if she called out.

'Come in!' she called. 'The door's open.'

There was a brief moment of silence, then the clicking of the old-fashioned latch. 'Hello!' The voice was dismayingly familiar and Cadie groaned inwardly when she heard it. Standing up there on the dresser, clad in that same old voluminous apron, she felt an utter fool. Why, oh, why did it have to be Robert? 'Cadie! Where are you?'

'In the kitchen!' She clung to the shelf and wished herself miles away.

'Busy with the—' He appeared in the doorway a second later, his expression curious, swiftly changing to explosive laughter when he saw her predicament. 'What the hell are you doing up there?' he asked.

'Learning to fly!' She glared down at him, only

casually noticing the big bouquet of roses he carried with something else wrapped in gilt paper.

He put his packages down on the kitchen table and came to stand just below her, his hands on his hips, his blond head tipped back, regarding her quizzically. 'Then you'd better fly down from your perch,' he told her.

'Oh, don't be idiotic!'

'It was your suggestion that you could fly,' he reminded her.

'I'm stuck up here.'

'Aah! Too bad!' He was obviously in no hurry to proffer assistance, but instead sat himself on the edge of the table and folded his arms.

It was the first time she had seen him quite so casually dressed, and the white trousers and tee shirt he wore did wonders for his tan and his blond hair. He looked unbelievably attractive, she thought, and pulled herself up hastily in case she really did become weak at the knees, as Gordon had suggested.

'You *could* help me down,' she told him.

'So I could.'

'If you'll put the steps back again I can manage.'

He looked at the fallen steps, kicking them carelessly. 'If they collapsed as easily as that,' he told her, 'they're not safe to use again. Much better to get rid of them.' He proceeded to do just that, while Cadie watched him wide-eyed and unbelieving as he took the steps to the back door and flung them out into the garden with a resounding clatter.

He came back rubbing his hands and smiling satisfaction. 'And now how am I supposed to get down from here?' Cadie asked, and he grinned.

'Hmm, that's a thought.' He rubbed his chin with one hand. 'I suppose I could have your typewriter brought over and you could work from there.'

'*Will* you be serious?' It was almost impossible to stamp her foot in her position, but somehow she managed it, and he shook his head and tut-tutted disapprovingly.

'Temper!' he admonished.

'You're enough to try the temper of a saint,' Cadie retorted.

'And you're no saint!'

'I don't claim to be, and if you don't help me down I shall take these pots and pans one by one and throw them at your head.'

'Ooh!' He shook his head at her, then came and stood by the dresser again. 'Come on, Humpty Dumpty, before you fall.'

He reached up for her, but Cadie shook her head, hestitating. 'I—'

'Come *on*,' he urged. 'You don't imagine I can't lift a little shrimp like you, do you?'

She hesitated a second longer, then bent down, and he put his hands under her arms, swinging her down easily, although she squeaked in alarm when her feet left the dresser. 'O.K.?'

He still held her, his hands at her waist, and he was so close that she could see the tiny lines of laughter at the corners of his eyes. She nodded. 'Yes, thank you.'

He slid his hands down to her back and pushed her

closer to him, and Cadie's heart was beating a wild tattoo as she sought to avoid his gaze. 'Is that the best you can do when I saved you from certain death, or at least a broken neck?' he asked, and she knew he was laughing at her because it was in his voice, and his eyes too if she had dared to look at him.

'I – I don't know what more you expect of me,' she told him. 'Please let me go, Mr. Dean.'

'For a start,' he said, making no effort to release her, 'you can call me Rob, instead of that madly precise Mr. Dean you always insist on.'

'You *are* my employer.'

'So's Gordon, in a sense,' he retorted, 'but you never call him Mr. Charles, do you?'

'No.'

'Then why not treat me the same way?'

'Please—' She put her hands and tried to break his hold on her, but he held her firm.

'Rob,' he insisted.

'Please let me go!'

'You are *stubborn*, aren't you?'

She risked an upward glance and found the light grey eyes much too close for comfort. 'And you're *not*, I suppose?' she retorted.

'Not stubborn,' he denied. 'On me it's just a strong will.' Cadie flushed, pushing at him, trying to free herself.

'That nasty, arrogant sex discrimination again!' she declared. 'You infuriate me!'

'So I gather.' He seemed quite unperturbed by the idea, and Cadie was no nearer freeing herself. In fact she was suddenly held even more tightly as he drew her closer to him until he bent his head and brought his mouth down over hers, hard and self-confident, holding her so tight she could not have moved even had she tried.

It began to dawn on her suddenly that she had offered no resistance whatever, she had even responded initially, and she fought to free herself, as angry with herself as she was with him. 'Oh, you—!' Her blue eyes blazed darkly and her breathing was so uneven she could not get the words out properly. 'I – I ought to – I could—' She snatched off the cotton square that covered her head and stood for a second trying to still the wild uncontrollable pulse that pounded in her temple.

He laughed then. He actually laughed, and Cadie looked around for something to throw at him. The first thing that came to hand was the bouquet of roses he had put down on the table and she picked them up unseeingly and held them aloft, only hesitating when he held up a hand.

'Don't spoil your roses,' he said, and Cadie looked at them, blinking surprise when she realized what she was holding.

'Mine?' she asked huskily, because her throat was suddenly dry.

He nodded. 'Yours.'

She held them for several seconds, looking at the soft pink blooms, then impulsively lifted them to her face and held them softly to her cheek. 'They're beautiful,' she said, and glanced at him, suspicious again. 'Are you sure they're mine?'

'Quite sure,' he replied. 'Why do you suppose I brought them over here otherwise?'

'But—'

'They're by way of a thank you for bringing me luck last night,' he told her.

'Oh, I see.' She felt guilty again then, because she should have been Gordon's mascot and it had not worked for Gordon as it had for Robert.

'The chocolates are yours too,' he said. 'You like dark ones, don't you?'

'Yes. Yes, I do.' She felt oddly shy suddenly and wished she could do something about the way her heart was behaving. He came closer now that her temper was safely over, quickly as it always was. 'How did you know what I like?' she asked, and he smiled.

'I asked Dottie.'

'Oh.' She inhaled the fragrance of the roses again and looked at him from under her lashes. 'Thank you.'

'What else?'

The grey-eyed gaze held hers steadily, and she took a very deep breath before she replied, 'Thank you, Rob.'

'That's my girl!' He brushed his lips against her forehead. 'And don't you ever let me catch you using those ruddy steps again, or I'll break your neck myself and save you the trouble.'

'That'll rather defeat the object, won't it?' she asked, and he laughed.

'You won't use them again, will you, Cadie?' he said,

sobering suddenly. 'I'd no idea the wretched things were here, and in that condition.'

'They didn't seem too bad.'

'They're dangerous,' he insisted, and smiled wryly. 'In fact I don't think I'll trust you not to do something else daft,' he added. 'I'll bung them in the boot of the car and take them out of your way.'

'Oh, really!' Cadie exclaimed. 'You'd think I was a helpless baby!'

He put a hand to her face and stroked her cheek. 'Aren't you?' he asked softly.

'No! No, I'm not.'

He remained like that for several seconds, his fingers gently caressing her cheek, then suddenly pulled himself up and laughed shortly. 'Oh well, I'd better leave you to get on with your chores,' he told her. 'You're going out with Gordon this afternoon, aren't you?'

'Yes.' She was a little surprised that he knew, and she must have shown it, for he smiled knowingly.

'He was full of it at breakfast,' he told her. 'And he asked Mrs. Calthrop for a picnic tea for two.'

'I see.'

He collected up the steps from the back garden and carried them under one arm. 'You – you like Gordon?' He paused briefly in his stride, and it was so unlike him to be hesitant about anything that she looked at him curiously for a moment before she answered.

'Yes, I like him.'

'He—' He hesitated again, then pushed his free hand through his hair and shook his head. 'None of my

66

business,' he said briskly. 'I'll say it before you do.' He was half-way to the door before she could even think of an answer, and she followed him as he made for the front door, wondering at his uncharacteristic behaviour. He turned as he opened the door and shot one eyebrow upwards, laughing softly. 'Be good!' he told her.

It was almost exactly three o'clock when Gordon came for her that afternoon, and Dottie opened the door to him, her expression exaggeratedly coy. 'She's ready for you,' she told him.

Cadie picked up her handbag and smiled as he came into the room, casual and very good-looking in blue slacks and a white shirt. 'Hello, Gordon.'

His eyes paid tribute to the simple yellow dress that flattered her colouring and her figure, and he smiled appreciatively. 'You look lovely,' he said.

'Of course she does,' Dottie informed him, before Cadie could reply. 'I was always green with envy at the way she could wear anything and look stunning.'

'Oh, nonsense,' Cadie laughed. 'Looks are purely superficial. You have traits that I envy much more.'

'Huh! Like what?'

'Like a nice placid temperament, for one thing,' Cadie told her. 'You never fly off the handle like I do, do you?'

'Not often,' Dottie admitted. 'But I never seem to have reason to.'

'And you worked for Rob for nearly eighteen months?'

She was not really aware of the way Gordon's eyes narrowed briefly when she used his stepbrother's christian name, she was talking to Dottie, and she had her attention.

'Oh, never with Rob,' Dottie declared, as if such a thing was impossible. 'He was an absolute love to work for.'

'Then he's changed since you left,' Cadie retorted, laughing at her friend's expression.

'I don't believe it,' Dottie declared stoutly. 'He bought you chocolates and roses, didn't he? *That's* not ordinary perks in the average office, love.'

'Roses?' Gordon was watching her narrowly and Cadie realized where this bit of teasing byplay had got her. Obviously Robert had said nothing about bringing her flowers and chocolates.

She looked at Gordon, determinedly open and honest about it, in case he should think she had a reason to hide anything from him. 'He came to see me this morning,' she told him, 'and brought me a thank-you present for bringing him luck last night.'

'I'm not surprised he saw the need to do something,' Gordon replied shortly. 'He must have been mad to have taken a chance like he did with all that money. You *must* have brought him luck, I only wish you could have done as well for me.'

'Oh, well,' Dottie told him cheerfully, 'it's all in the family, isn't it?' A sentiment Gordon did not altogether appreciate.

'Not in this instance it isn't,' he said. 'And he never said a word about going to see Cadie this morning.'

'Perhaps he didn't think it was important enough to make a song and dance about,' Cadie told him shortly, and he had the grace to look a little ashamed of his mood.

'I still can't think why he had to come over and bring you flowers and chocolates,' Gordon complained some time later as they drove out to Dorly Point, and Cadie's heart sank at the prospect of having him in a bad humour for the remainder of the afternoon.

'It's not that important, surely,' she said with a sigh of annoyance.

'I don't like having him bring my girl presents,' he told her. 'How would he like it if I gave Lida roses and chocolates? *And* sneaked off on a Sunday morning to give them to her.'

Cadie smiled, despite her irritation. 'From what I've seen of Rob with Mellida Dawson,' she said, 'he wouldn't care less.'

'Oh?' He frowned anew at the opinion. 'Why's that?'

Cadie shrugged. 'Oh – I don't know, the way he spoke to her.'

'Well, don't let him fool you with that take-it-or-leave-it attitude he adopts,' he told her. 'He'll marry Lida sooner or later, because she's made up her mind he will – and Lida always gets what she wants.'

'Oh, does she?'

'You bet she does. She's had two husbands already, and Rob's lined up as number three. He hasn't a chance against Lida, she's dynamite.'

'Well, maybe she's lit the wrong fuse this time!'

Cadie could not imagine what had made her pass such a rash opinion, and Gordon glanced at her briefly, his brows arched in surprise. 'You sound very sure,' he said.

'I – I just think he's not as interested in her as she likes to think he is, that's all,' she told him, and he laughed abruptly and with little humour. 'It's only guesswork, or a woman's intuition, whatever you like to call it.'

'I see. As long as you have no more personal grounds for saying it.'

She looked at him hastily. 'Of course I haven't. You know Rob and I seldom see eye to eye on anything. We haven't not from the first moment he -- I ran into his car.'

'Yet all of a sudden he's Rob instead of Mr. Dean as he's been until now.'

Cadie sighed deeply. 'As he pointed out to me this morning,' she explained, 'you're almost as much my employer as he is, and I call you by your christian name, so he didn't see why he wasn't entitled to the same.'

'And you agreed?'

'I agreed for the sake of peace,' she said, 'although I'm not sure it's good office discipline. Now please can we forget about him, Gordon, and enjoy our ride?'

'Of course, I'm sorry.' He turned a rueful smile on her. 'I get a bit jealous of him sometimes,' he confessed. 'I suppose because he seems to have everything land on his lap. But I suppose I should have known better than to think you'd be likely to fall for his well practised charm, shouldn't I?'

Cadie merely nodded. The memory of her reaction to Robert's kiss was still too fresh in her mind for her to be too adamant about that.

'It was nearly a nasty incident, wasn't it?' Dottie said, the following evening when Cadie sat with her while Michael was out. 'I hope I didn't involve you in anything very awkward, love.'

Cadie smiled and shook her head. 'Nothing I couldn't handle,' she assured her. 'I don't like Gordon treating me as if he owns me.'

'Mmm.' Dottie mused, 'he is inclined to be a bit possessive in his own little way.'

'Did—' Cadie paused, finding it a bit difficult to put into words what she wanted to ask. 'Did he ever take you out, Dottie?'

'Oh yes,' Dottie said airily. 'Several times, but I'm not really his type, any more than I am Rob's. They go for the strictly glamorous sort.' She giggled. 'And that lets me out, love.'

'Oh, Dottie, I do wish you'd stop making yourself out to be some sort of monster!'

'So I shall be in another couple of months,' Dottie giggled.

'You're a pretty and attractive girl,' Cadie told her, refusing to be sidetracked. 'So stop talking as if you're a plain Jane with no redeeming features, or I'll tell Michael and he'll tell you off.'

'He would too,' Dottie said, her eyes shining as she twirled her wedding ring round and round on her finger. 'He thinks I'm the last word, bless him.'

'Of course he does.'

'You wait until it happens to you,' Dottie told her. 'It's the most marvellous feeling, Cadie. All sort of warm and tummy-turning, and you feel like Cleopatra even when you know you look like the side of a house.'

Cadie had a momentary vision of herself clad in a huge print overall with her hair tied up in a scarf and a grimy face, being kissed by Robert Dean, who only liked the glamorous type, according to Dottie. A hasty blink and a mental dig in the ribs brought her back swiftly to reality and she smiled at Dottie's round, happy face.

'I can't wait,' was all she said.

CHAPTER FIVE

IT was nearly a week later, while Cadie was intent on trying to interpret some of Robert's more indecipherable script, that he suddenly looked across at her and broke into her concentration.

'Are you doing anything tomorrow night?' he asked, and Cadie blinked for a moment, her thoughts still with the script she was typing.

'I – I'm sorry?'

Robert smiled. 'I asked you if you were doing anything tomorrow night,' he said. 'Has Gordon arranged anything for the two of you?'

'No. No, he hasn't, not as far as I know.' It was annoying to feel so suddenly breathless and expectant and she hoped he would not recognize it.

'Then would you like to come up to town with me?'

'To London?'

He lifted his shoulders. 'Where else?'

'I – I don't know,' she demurred, wondering what on earth lay behind such a sudden and unexpected invitation.

'Oh, it's all right,' he assured her with a wicked grin. 'I haven't got evil designs on your honour, so you needn't look so wary.'

'I wasn't looking wary,' Cadie denied hastily.

'You looked as if you suspected the worst,' he told

her, and laughed when she tightened her mouth.

'Whatever the worst is, I was expecting no such thing,' she informed him shortly. 'I was just wondering—' She looked at him from under her lashes. 'I was just wondering why you'd asked *me*?'

'Why shouldn't I ask you?' he parried. 'You're free, beautiful and over the age of consent, and Gordon hasn't got a monopoly on your time, has he?'

'No. No, of course not.'

'And I have two tickets for the new Ballard show tomorrow night, so what else need I say? You'd like to see it, wouldn't you?'

'I'd love to see it, I've heard such a lot about it.'

'Good. That's settled that – be ready in your glad rags about half past five and I'll pick you up, that should give us good time and allow for any last-minute feminine panics about missing jewellery and zippers that won't work.'

'You make it sound inevitable,' she said, unable to resist a smile. 'I don't have much trouble like that as a rule. *Now* I suppose I'd better touch wood.'

'You'd better,' he agreed.

'There's only one thing,' Cadie remarked, looking through her lashes at him again. 'I don't usually leave here until half past five.'

'Well, don't worry about that,' he told her. 'I'll have a word with your boss and get him to let you go about four. O.K.?'

'O.K.' She was longing to ask why she had been so honoured and not Mellida Dawson, whom she knew for a fact was 'resting' at the moment, waiting for a new television play to go into rehearsal. What she would say if she ever found out about the outing did not bear thinking about. Gordon, she thought, would not be exactly pleased with the idea either.

'Are we going – are we going very grand?' she ventured, after a few seconds. 'I just wondered what I should wear,' she added hastily when he cocked a brow at her.

'Oh, I see. We're not going too grand, as you call it, but I know just the thing for you to wear.'

'Oh?' She eyed him warily.

'That stunning silver grey number you wore to the gambling club that night. That does things for both of us. Can you wear that again?'

'Of course.' Her heart was doing impossible things when she caught his eye briefly. 'It's my favourite dress, as it happens.'

'You look rather like a princess out of the Arabian Nights in that,' he told her. 'And you smelled rather gorgeous too. Could we have some more of the same perfume too?'

'It's my special occasion one,' she told him. 'I think it could be arranged.'

'You don't mind me stating a preference?' he asked, and Cadie shook her head, her brain spinning chaotically with all this special interest in her looks.

'No, of course not. I'm flattered you remember either.'

'When you brought me such luck at the tables? Oh, Cadie, don't be so mock modest.' He caught and held her gaze, his light eyes bright and startling in the brown

75

of his face. 'No man is likely to forget how you looked in that dress.' He laughed softly. 'Or in any other dress, for that matter, if I'm honest.'

'Even my old apron?' She spoke impulsively, and he laughed again, in such a way that she could feel the colour in her cheeks and hastily lowered her eyes.

'Especially in that old apron,' he said. 'You must know that.'

It was Gordon's entrance at that moment that saved her from further embarrassment, and he glanced suspiciously from one to the other before he spoke. 'Am I interrupting?'

'Nothing important,' Robert assured him. 'What crisis have we hit now?'

'It's Lida,' Gordon said. 'She's on the phone, not exactly a crisis, but she wants to speak to you and I wondered if you were free.'

'If she wants anything altering in that script, I'm not,' Robert told him bluntly. 'She knows I don't re-write to suit anybody.'

'I don't think it's that,' Gordon told him. 'It's something about some bod with a painting you wanted.'

'Oh yes.' He nodded. 'Put her through here, will you, Gordon, please?' His sigh was more resigned than flattering as he waited for his call to be put through. '*Now* she rings,' he said, to nobody in particular.

The conversation was short and, on Robert's side at least, almost monosyllabic, and he put the receiver down when he had finished with a small, rather rueful smile on his face, flicking a brief glance at Cadie and catching her eye.

'Things could,' he said slowly, pulling at his lower lip thoughtfully, 'get rather interesting.'

Cadie was faced with a rather indignant Gordon that same evening, and she wished she could have found some other reason for refusing his invitation to dinner the following night, without letting him know that she was going to the theatre with Robert.

She could, she supposed, have taken the chance of his not finding out and given him some other excuse, but it seemed rather silly in view of their relationship. After all, she was not committed to Gordon in any way, and there was no reason at all why she should not go out with Robert if he asked her, although it was doubtful if Gordon would see it like that.

'Of all the nerve!' he exclaimed, when she told him of her plans. 'How he can have the nerve to ask you out when he knows perfectly well that you're—'

'I'm someone you take out sometimes, Gordon,' she said quietly, before he could voice anything more possessive.

He looked a little taken aback for a moment, then nodded slowly. 'I suppose I am taking a lot for granted,' he admitted. 'I always think of you as my girl.'

'Always? You've known me only a very short time,' she said, and smiled understanding. 'I can't say much about being impulsive,' she admitted. 'I'm as bad myself, but please don't be in too much of a hurry, Gordon.'

'Am I? In too much of a hurry?'

'I think so, at the moment. I like you, I like you a lot, but it's too soon yet to say I want to be so serious that I can't go out with anyone else sometimes.'

'Like Rob?'

She nodded. 'Like Rob,' she agreed. 'After all, he *is* my boss and if he asks me to go to the theatre with him I can't just turn him down flat for no reason at all, even if wanted to.'

'Which you don't.'

'No, I don't, quite honestly. I'm quite looking forward to it, as a matter of fact. I haven't been to a show for some time, and a new Ballard show is something of an event.'

'It is,' he agreed wryly, 'and trust Rob to get tickets when everyone else is queueing up for them!' He frowned then, as if something had only now occurred to him. 'That's odd, too,' he said. 'Why isn't he taking Lida? She's been trying to get tickets, I know.'

'I wouldn't know.' She had a sudden uneasy and discomfiting suspicion at the back of her mind, but she did not voice it to Gordon. 'He was talking to her on the phone just after he invited me to go with him.'

'This morning when she rang?' Cadie nodded. 'Did he mention it to her?'

'No.'

'Whew!' He smiled, a rather malicious smile as he mused on something for a moment, then he laughed shortly. 'Oh ho! You just wait until Lida finds out he had tickets and he didn't take her,' he said. 'She'll blow him sky high!'

The thought that Mellida Dawson would blow Robert sky high did not amuse Cadie as much as it did Gordon. For one thing, she thought ruefully, she would probably be the main object of the actress's anger, not Robert, and the prospect was more daunting than amusing. If Mellida Dawson felt the way Gordon said she did about Robert, then any other woman he took out, however innocently, would be in for a pretty rough time.

All that day Cadie tried to think of some excuse that would let her back out of the proposed visit. Some reasonable excuse that Robert would accept without suspicion, but she could think of nothing that was plausible enough to fool him, and always, at the back of her mind, was the growing certainty that she really wanted to go with him. Whether Gordon and Mellida Dawson approved or not.

At four o'clock Robert looked across at her, still deeply engrossed in work, and he whistled softly, 'Cadie!'

She looked up, eyes wide, not realizing for a moment why he had called her. 'Yes?'

'Four o'clock.' He tapped his wrist watch with one finger. 'Time for Cinderella to change into her ball gown.'

'Oh. Oh yes, I hadn't realized.'

He watched her as she tidied her desk and covered her machine, a curious half smile on his lips, his fingers steepled to support his chin. 'You don't sound very enthusiastic,' he told her, as she picked up her handbag ready to go. 'Have you changed your mind about wanting to come? Or has Gordon changed it for you?'

'Neither.' She met his eyes, though she would rather not have done in the circumstances. 'You're wrong, imagining things you don't hear.'

'Hmm. Maybe.' He smiled then and nodded dismissal. 'Off you go. You've got an hour and a half to have a bite to eat and paint the lily, but don't overdo either. We'll be having supper after the show and it shouldn't take you long to achieve the Arabian Nights look.'

'I'll be ready.'

He watched her out of the room, and she wondered at the heady lilt of excitement she felt as she closed the door behind her. It was not as if she had never been to a show before, or as if she was a young girl on her first date. Her lighthearted anticipation was something that needed some explaining, but she was not going to attempt to explain it now.

She saw Gordon as she went through the hall and he came across to her, putting his hands on her arms, his face looking rather sulky as he looked down at her. 'I wish you were coming with me,' he said. 'But I hope you enjoy it, Cadie.'

'Thank you. I'm sure I shall,' she told him. 'I'm looking forward to it.'

'You'll be back late?'

She nodded. 'Almost certainly – we're having a meal after the show.'

'Yes, of course.'

She could not resist a smile for the air of determined gloom he wore. 'Gordon! Don't look as if it's the end of the world! I'm only going to the theatre with Rob, not

— not eloping with him.'

'I'm sorry.'

'I can see you tomorrow night instead, if you'd like,' she told him.

'I wish I could,' he lamented. 'I have to go to town myself tomorrow afternoon on some business for Rob.'

'Oh, I see.'

'You know I manage his affairs as well as assisting with the research,' he told her, and she nodded. 'That's one of the drawbacks at times like this. *I* have to go galloping off to town on *his* business affairs while he's free to date my girl.'

His self-pitying gloom was too much for Cadie and, although she felt rather unkind for doing it, she was unable to resist a gentle laugh. 'I'm sorry,' she told him when he looked at her reproachfully, 'but you do look so determinedly hard done by, Gordon, and you're not really.'

'If I *can* get back fairly early will you wait, just in case?'

She smiled. 'Yes, of course I will.'

'Promise?'

She laughed softly, holding up a hand in oath. 'Promise.' She glanced at her watch and impulsively tiptoed to kiss him. 'I must hurry, Gordon, or I'll be late as he expects me to be, and I can't let him be right about that.'

'I'll see you tomorrow?'

'If you're back in time, yes.'

'I'll make it my business to be back early.'

She heard a sound of movement from the office behind them and hastily went across the hall and out of the front door before Robert appeared.

She was ready in plenty of time, since nothing went wrong with her preparations, and she sat in the armchair by the window waiting for her escort to arrive, rather pleased that she was the one having to wait. After his remarks about women taking a long time to get ready she could justifiably take reasonable pleasure in proving him wrong, she thought.

He arrived at precisely half past five and when she answered the door to him he whistled softly in appreciation at the sight of her. 'You look and smell delicious,' he told her, and Cadie could not resist a smile.

'You make me sound rather like an apple pie,' she informed him.

'Oh, you're something much more exotic than an apple pie. I think I shall call you Scheherazade, it suits you better than anything else I can think of.'

'You don't have to think of anything,' Cadie told him, 'I already have a name.'

'But you're just as I've always imagined the beautiful and crafty Scheherazade would be, sitting there telling all those thousand and one tales to her poor benighted husband just to save her neck,' he told her. 'You look so tiny, feminine and beautiful, and I'll bet you're as crafty and knowing as a cartload of monkeys.'

Cadie flushed, clutching her purse in both hands, her eyes indignant. 'You have no cause to say that,' she objected. 'And if you're going to spend the entire evening make rude remarks about me I shall refuse to come!'

'And go somewhere with Gordon instead?' he asked, and laughed when she looked reproachful. 'I'm sorry, Cadie.' He put an arm round her shoulders in an unexpected gesture of affection and drew her towards the door. 'I promise not to tease you.'

The night was warm and bright with stars and Robert drove not too fast, making the journey enjoyable, although they spoke little. Not that their silence was an antagonistic one, but it seemed much too lovely a night to need conversation, and she found him an unexpectedly easy companion.

He glanced at her once as they reached the outskirts of London and one brow briefly questioned her silence. 'All right?' he asked, and Cadie nodded.

'It's a lovely night again.'

'Lovely,' he agreed. 'Are you glad you came after all?'

She glanced at him curiously. 'After all?' she queried. 'Was it ever in doubt that I'd come?'

Again he spared her a brief glance over one shoulder. 'I don't know,' he parried. 'Was it?'

Cadie shook her head. 'I've never had any doubts about coming,' she informed him. 'I wanted to see the show, and you asked me to come with you—'

'And you hesitated initially,' he interposed swiftly. 'Remember?'

'Only for a second,' she insisted. 'I – I wasn't sure why you'd asked *me* to come.'

'And as I said at the time – why not?'

'Because—' She looked at him from under her lashes. At the strong profile, so self-confident, outlined against the night sky, and the thick, light mop of hair that was so distinctive.

'Because?' he prompted, and surprised her in her scrutiny so that she hastily averted her eyes.

'Because I would have expected you to bring Miss Dawson,' she said impulsively. 'Especially to this particular show. Gordon says she's been wanting to see it.'

'Oh, he did, did he?' A faint smile crooked his mouth at one corner. 'Well, for his, and your, information, Lida's going to be there tonight too. She's going with a friend of hers.'

'Oh, I see.'

'Do you?'

'I think so,' Cadie told him. 'That's probably what you meant by that – that enigmatic remark you made when you put the phone down after Miss Dawson rang you yesterday.' He said nothing, so she pressed on, watching surreptitiously from under her lashes. 'You said things could get very interesting.'

'Did I?'

'Yes, and I think I can see now what you meant by it.'

'Something not very flattering, is your opinion, no doubt.'

'Not very,' Cadie agreed rashly. 'But you probably *would* relish the idea of Mellida Dawson being very angry when she sees you with me.'

'Very angry is putting it rather mildly, I imagine,' he said, quite calmly. 'And I don't know that I'd relish it exactly, but since it's almost inevitable she will see us, it will be interesting to see what she does.'

'Interesting for you, perhaps,' Cadie retorted. 'But embarrassing for me.'

'I hope not.' He turned, his smile gleaming suddenly in his dark face. 'Why don't you make the most of it, Cadie? It's not every day a girl has the chance to put one over on Lida Dawson.'

'I don't want to put one over on her, as you call it,' Cadie informed him. 'And I hope that wasn't why you asked me to come with you, Rob.'

He negotiated a corner before he answered, and she thought his mouth looked a little tight-lipped at the suggestion. They were travelling along a lighted street now, and it was easier for her to see his face. 'I asked you to come because I wanted you to,' he said. 'Don't start attributing me with ulterior motives, Cadie.'

'I'm sorry.'

He flashed her a swift, encouraging smile over his shoulder. 'Don't start being sorry either,' he told her. 'There's no need.'

It was exciting to be among the theatre-going crowds. She had gone to the theatre sometimes when she lived in London, but not often enough to grow blasé about it, and Cadie felt the added excitement of being in distinguished company.

It was much different being escorted to stalls seats by a man as self-confident and striking-looking as Robert Dean than climbing up to the cheaper parts with a rather nervous and self-conscious escort who was as excited by the novelty of it as she was herself.

Robert Dean would have no doubt that the best seats were available to him, or that his companion would be eye-catching enough to turn heads. He accepted it all as his due and so did everyone else, it seemed.

Cadie accepted her new status with as much aplomb as she could muster, fully aware of the curious looks she drew from the people Robert greeted. He had no call to introduce her to any until the last interval when they were sitting in the stalls bar, then a tall, greying-haired man with bright, dark eyes spoke to him as he handed Cadie her drink.

'Rob! Long time no see!'

Her escort allowed his hand to be shaken although he showed little enthusiasm for the newcomer. 'Hello, Murton,' he said, and would probably have left it like that if the other man had not persisted.

'Haven't seen you for ages,' he told him. 'Everything O.K.?'

'Yes, thanks, fine.' Robert sipped his drink, looking as if he was waiting for the other man to leave, standing protectively half in front of Cadie.

'Gordon all right?'

'Yes, thanks.'

The other man laughed, a little self-consciously Cadie recognized. 'I don't have to ask after Lida, I know she's fine,' he told him. 'She's here with me.'

'I know.' Robert's light grey eyes held a glint of malice, Cadie could have sworn. 'She told me she was coming with you.'

'Oh. Oh, I see.' A brief sip of his drink fortified his confidence. 'Lida said you couldn't get tickets,' he went on. 'I managed to get hold of a couple and I know Lida wanted to see it, so I asked her to come with me.'

He sounded rather as if he was either apologizing or daring Robert to object, neither of which Robert showed the slightest sign of interest in. 'I hope she's enjoying it,' he said.

'Oh, she is.' He looked pointedly at Cadie. 'Are you enjoying it, Miss—?'

'Miss O'Connor,' Robert supplied quietly, taking another sip of his drink. 'Cadie's my secretary.' He smiled at her, and briefly lowered one eyelid, unseen by the other man. 'Cadie, this is Murton Stokes, an old acquaintance.'

But not an old friend, Cadie thought, as she shook hands with the man she now knew to be quite a well-known television producer. Evidently there was little love lost between the two men and she wondered if Mellida Dawson was the reason for their dislike.

To Cadie's relief the man's companion did not put in an appearance, and he went off after a second or two, almost as if he too feared the result if Mellida Dawson saw Robert there. Robert himself seemed quite unmoved and he finished his drink just as the bell went for the last act, taking her arm as they made their way back to their seats.

It was as they were leaving the theatre, however, that the actress suddenly came through the chattering crowd in the foyer and saw Robert, her instinctive smile of pleasure changing almost immediately to curiosity.

'Rob!' For the moment she had apparently not noticed Cadie, and she came up to him, hands outstretched in greeting, tiptoeing to kiss him, with Murton Stokes trailing behind her and looking oddly uneasy. Apparently he had said nothing to her about seeing Robert and Cadie in the bar.

'Hello, Lida.' Robert greeted her with a smile, but was not over-effusive. 'You remember Cadie, don't you?'

Mellida Dawson's sharp blue eyes recognized her at last, and Cadie tried to smile, although it was not very successful.

'Oh yes, Cadie O'Connor.' She repeated Cadie's name and smiled, as if she still found it amusing. 'The one with the odd name.' The sharp eyes flicked back again to Robert. 'Darling, you didn't tell me you were coming. I thought you couldn't get tickets for this show, now I find you here with this—'

'Cadie,' Robert said quietly but firmly. 'And I wish you'd keep your voice down, Lida, you're not on stage now.'

'Rob, you—' She drew a deep breath, fighting for control while Cadie could feel the colour warm in her cheeks, although no one in the noisy, crowded foyer seemed to be taking any undue notice of them. 'I suppose this is your idea of revenge,' Lida said between her teeth, and Robert shook his head. He was actually smiling now, Cadie noticed, as if he was relishing the moment as she had suspected he would. She had even, she remembered, apologized to him for suggesting it, and here he was proving her quite right after all.

'Oh, don't be childish, Lida,' he told the other woman, quite unperturbed by her obvious anger.

'Childish!' She looked at him for a few seconds, her hands clenching and unclenching over the clasp of her bag, then, unbelievably, she smiled, although it was obviously quite an effort. 'All right, darling,' she said at last. 'I know it was my fault for coming with Murton, but I *was* tempted when I knew he had tickets and he was *very* keen for me to come with him.'

Murton Stokes, Cadie noticed, looked almost as embarrassed as she felt herself. 'You don't have to explain Lida,' Robert told her, assured as ever. 'I brought Cadie, and I'm quite happy with the arrangement.'

'Even if you did have to take second best, poor darling.' A long slender hand caressed his face for a moment, and she smiled confidently. 'You could have rung me, Rob darling, and let me know you had tickets too. I could have deserted Murton and come with you.' She seemed uncaring that her companion could hear every word, and he looked both annoyed and embarrassed.

'I did ring you,' Robert told her. 'Several times, in fact, but you were out. By the time you rang me, it was too late.'

Too late, Cadie thought bitterly, because he had already asked her to go with him rather than be left without a partner for the evening. She could feel the blood pounding in her head as the humiliating fact sank in deeper and she wanted to get away from that crowded place, and from him as fast as she could.

'Excuse me!' She heard herself whisper the words and pushed her way through the crowd towards the street door. Suddenly the noise and bustle of the foyer seemed unfriendly and oppressive and she needed some air, even though it was heavy with traffic fumes and almost sultrily hot.

She stood for a moment, uncertain just what she had meant to do, tempted even to hail a passing taxi and just disappear, but instead she simply stood there with her hands tight on the clasp of her purse. It would serve him right if she walked off and left him. It would probably be the first time anything like that had happened to him and it would do him good. Make him take things less for granted, especially the compliance of his secretary.

'Cadie!' Hard strong fingers curled round her arm and she was pulled up close to him. 'You weren't thinking of deserting me, were you?'

She shook her head in swift denial, although it had been uppermost in her mind only a moment since. 'I – I needed some air, that's all.'

'I expect you need your supper too,' he said, and would have led her out into the street, but she resisted for a moment, looking up at the strong, brown face with its light eyes regarding her curiously.

'I – I don't think I want any supper,' she told him. 'I'd like to go home, if you don't mind.'

His mouth tightened ominously and he looked at her down the length of his nose. Obviously such a situation was new to him and he disliked it intensely. 'I do mind,' he told her. 'I want my supper, and I refuse to eat at a table for two alone, so you'll have to come too.'

'Are you worried about your reputation?' Cadie asked, her eyes darkly angry.

'Why, you—' His anger matched her own for a moment, then he laughed shortly. 'I see,' he said softly. 'You're getting your own back for Lida.'

'Can you blame me?'

He looked at her steadily for a moment, then smiled. 'I don't quite know what to do about you,' he confessed at last. 'You puzzle me, and I don't mind admitting it.'

'I can't think why,' Cadie told him. 'Anyone would take exception to being made to look a – a fool like I was, not to mention Mr. Stokes, although he's apparently prepared to accept it for the pleasure of being with Mellida Dawson.'

'And you're prepared to fight to your last breath to prove that—' He cocked a quizzical brow at her. 'What *are* you trying to prove, Cadie?'

'I'm trying to prove nothing,' she insisted. 'I just don't like suddenly realizing that I – I was second best, that's all. It's not a very pleasant sensation when it dawns on you. And I *was* second best, wasn't I, Rob?' She hated the way her voice quavered when she asked him that, because it betrayed her dislike of the fact that she had been hurt to discover she was only a stand-in for Mellida Dawson.

He did not answer for a moment, but looked at her steadily until she lowered her eyes. 'It depends what you mean by second best,' he said at last. 'If you mean that I tried to contact Lida to let her know I had the tickets for tonight, you're right, I did. But only because I knew she was so keen to see it. It was quite true what I told her, however, that I'm quite satisfied with the present arrangement. I'm delighted to be able to show off the most beautiful girl in town, and I refuse to believe you've ever been second best to anybody.'

It was working, Cadie thought in a panic. That indefinable magic he seemed able to dispense to order and which always made her feel as if she had misjudged him. 'I don't—' she began, but he raised her fingers to his lips, a glint of the familiar laughter deep in his eyes as he challenged her to argue further.

'Come along, Scheherazade,' he said softly, 'the peacocks' tongues and spicy wines await you and we have only one night, not a thousand and one.'

Cadie hesitated for only a second, then followed him out into the night, her hand still held tightly in his, a small brief thought for Gordon crossing her mind — until Robert looked down at her and smiled.

CHAPTER SIX

CADIE answered the telephone because she was alone in the office, although she did hesitate for a moment because it was so unusual for a call to be put straight through. As a rule the calls went to the telephone in the hall and were then put through to Robert's office, if he wanted to take them. He disliked being interrupted when he was working.

She lifted the receiver at last and gave the number, and a sharp, rather querulous voice answered her. 'Who *is* that?' The voice was unmistakable and Cadie felt her fingers tighten on the instrument instinctively.

'This is Cadie O'Connor, Miss Dawson. I'm afraid Mr. Dean isn't here at the moment.'

Mellida Dawson tutted impatiently. 'Well, where is he?'

'I'm not sure,' Cadie told her, wondering if she should offer to fetch Robert from his belated lunch. She was not sure what kind of a reception such an interruption would get, for even after three weeks of working for him, she was still a little wary of disobeying his explicit instructions and they had been, in this instance, that he was not to be disturbed by anything or anybody until he had eaten.

'You're not sure?' The voice sounded angry and scornful, as if she suspected delaying tactics. 'Well, go and see if you can find him, and if you can't, ask

Gordon if *he* knows where he is.'

'I – I'm not sure, Miss Dawson, you see—'

'I don't care what you think I see,' Mellida Dawson snapped. 'You go and find Rob for me, and hurry up about it! I don't have all day to stand here while you make up your mind to do as you're told.'

'Certainly, Miss Dawson.' Cadie banged the receiver down heavily on the desk and hoped the resulting thud had its desired effect at the other end.

Mrs. Calthrop was just coming out of the kitchen when she opened the door into the hall and Cadie smiled her relief. She had no intention of disturbing Robert personally if it could possibly be avoided, and Mrs. Calthrop was just the person to do it for her.

'I've got Miss Dawson on the phone,' she explained, 'and she insists on speaking to Mr. Dean. I'm wondering if he'll speak to her.'

'And you'd like me to go and ask him, is that it, love?'

'I'd rather you did,' Cadie admitted. 'He's less likely to bite your head off than mine.'

'Oh, I'm used to him,' the housekeeper told her with a smile. 'I'll tell him, don't worry.'

Cadie waited in the hall; she had no intention of becoming involved in any further back-biting with Mellida Dawson. She'd wait and see what message the housekeeper brought back and, if it was a refusal, she would more than willingly hand it on. But it was Robert, not Mrs. Calthrop, who appeared a few seconds later, and he smiled knowingly when he saw her waiting in the hall.

'What did you tell her?' he asked, giving her no time

94

to answer, but striding into the office and picking up the telephone. 'Hello, Lida.'

The instrument babbled for a moment and a surreptitious glance revealed a small smile crooking Robert's mouth as he listened. 'You must have it wrong,' he said, when the chattering paused, and added impatiently when it began again, 'Forget it, Lida, what did you call me about?'

He listened and answered briefly for several minutes, the woman at the other end seeming to do most of the talking, then he turned and winked an eye at Cadie as the voice grew shrill again. 'Yes, all right', he said at last. 'I'll put her on bread and water for a week. 'Bye, Lida.' He replaced the receiver and sat down at his desk, while Cadie watched him from under her lashes curiously. The last reference, she felt sure had concerned her, but she could scarcely ask him what it was all about, however curious she was.

'Aren't you curious?'

She glanced up a few seconds later, and saw him bent over his work, only the top of his blond head visible to her. 'I beg your pardon?'

He looked up then, a half smile on his face, his eyes quizzical. 'I said, aren't you curious?'

Cadie hesitated. 'Should I be?'

'Question for question! Don't you want to know why I'm putting you on bread and water for a week?'

'Oh, that. I can guess,' she replied shortly, and rolled another sheet of paper into her machine.

'I thought you might.' He laughed, still watching

her. 'I suppose you've been having one of your little protests again, haven't you?'

'You can say that if you like.'

'Lida claims you nearly deafened her, though I'm inclined to take that with a pinch of salt. Not that I can't sympathize with her to a certain extent,' he added with a grin. 'I know what it sounds like when somebody slams a receiver down at the other end.'

Cadie regarded him steadily for a moment. 'Are you telling me off?' she asked.

'No.'

'Oh. It sounded rather as if you were.'

'Do you think I *should* tell you off?'

Cadie gave her attention to the next line she was to type and refused to be drawn into quarrelling with him. 'No,' she said, 'but I'm sure Miss Dawson expects you to.'

'And you think I always do as Lida expects me to? You should know me better than that by now, Cadie.'

Cadie said nothing for a moment, then she looked across at him and pursed her lips. 'I don't think I'll ever know you,' she informed him solemnly. 'You're too much of an enigma for me to fathom.'

'Hmm.' He held her gaze and after a second or two she could feel the inevitable throb of pulse at her temple. 'I'm not sure whether to be flattered or not by that,' he told her. 'By the way, do you know anything about boats?'

The question was so sudden and so unexpected that she looked at him rather vaguely for a moment. 'Only that they go on water and float,' she said at last.

'Why?'

He shrugged. 'Pity.'

'Is it important?'

He smiled slowly and pulled a wry face at her. 'I was going to ask you to play second best again,' he confessed, and Cadie saw his reason at last.

'Miss Dawson can't go sailing with you,' she guessed, and he nodded.

'Right. I wondered if you'd step into her shoes and come with me, but if you can't—'

She shook her head, almost childishly pleased to be able to refuse him this time. She had not the slightest desire to take Mellida Dawson's place again in any way at all, and certainly not in a boat, for she knew absolutely nothing about them and would almost certainly make a complete fool of herself if she tried.

'I couldn't have come anyway,' she told him. 'I'm booked for Saturday *and* Sunday.'

'Gordon?'

She nodded. 'Yes, Gordon.'

He made a steeple of his fingers and rested his chin on them, his expression thoughtful, a hint of speculation in his eyes. 'Two days is being rather greedy,' he told her, although he didn't specify who was at fault. 'I suppose I'd be very unpopular if I shanghaied him to be my crew on Sunday?'

Cadie looked at him suspiciously. 'You – you wouldn't, would you?'

He laughed. 'I would you know, I'm entering for the round the coast race next month and I need the practice, there isn't much time.'

'But – but Gordon wouldn't come. He wouldn't let me down just to go sailing with you.'

'Do you want to bet on it?' he asked softly, his eyes gleaming. 'Gordon knows which side his bread's buttered, my sweet. He'll come if I crack the whip hard enough.'

'You monster!' Cadie declared flatly. 'You horrible, selfish monster! You'd do anything to get your own way, wouldn't you?'

'Anything,' he agreed, unruffled. 'Of course,' he added, 'I'd raise no objections at all if he brought you along too.'

'Oh, you wouldn't?'

'None at all,' he affirmed. 'In fact you'd add a very decorative touch.'

'Well, I'd as soon not come, and neither will Gordon if I ask him not to.'

He shook his head, a gleam of determination in the steady gaze he fixed her with. 'Oh, don't be so sure,' he told her. 'Don't try crossing swords with me, Cadie, I'm an old hand at demolishing any opposition.'

'I can imagine,' Cadie retorted. 'But I'm not easily over-awed, *Mr*. Dean, and I won't let you spoil my Sunday with Gordon, no matter how you try.'

'We'll see.' He bent his head over his work again and Cadie disliked the smile he wore, toying with the idea of throwing a dictionary at him. There was nothing she could do about Gordon at this very minute, but she would certainly do her best to make him keep to their arrangements for Sunday.

Her opportunity to mention the matter came that

same evening, but Gordon forestalled her by bringing up the subject himself. 'About Sunday,' he said as they strolled along the quay. 'How would you like to go sailing, instead of driving round to Dorly Point?'

'I wouldn't.' Her adamant answer startled him, she could tell, but she refused to yield one inch to Robert's pressure, however indirect.

'But, Cadie, you'd love it, honestly.'

'I wouldn't, I'd hate it.'

He looked so unhappy about it that she began to feel rather guilty. 'Do you get seasick?' he asked.

'No. But I'd rather go to Dorly Point, as we arranged.'

Again he was silent and Cadie kept her face determinedly averted so that she couldn't see his puzzled and rather worried expression. Apparently he had not expected any opposition and he was uncertain how to deal with it. Robert, she thought bitterly, could have shown him.

'Wouldn't you change your mind?' he begged. 'Just to please me.'

Cadie turned and looked at him. 'To please you I probably would,' she told him, 'but not to let Robert have his own way.'

'Oh! Oh, I see. He's mentioned it to you, has he?'

'He has,' Cadie agreed shortly. 'And he more or less told me he had only to crack the whip hard enough and you'd do as he said. He's not right, is he, Gordon?'

She was longing for him to deny it. To say it was nonsense and of course he would tell Robert where he got off, but instead he looked rather sheepish and gazed down at his feet as he walked. 'It's a bit difficult for me, Cadie,' he explained. 'You see – well, he got me out of a scrape once, more than once really, and I – truth is I suppose I owe him slave time, in a way.'

'Oh, I see.'

'I wish I *could* tell him to go to hell,' Gordon assured her with such feeling that she was bound to believe him. 'But – well, I can't in all fairness, Cadie. Please understand.'

Cadie sighed. 'Oh, I understand,' she said resignedly. 'I understand that he's more or less blackmailing you with some misdemeanour you'd much rather forget. It's typical of him.'

'Oh no, really, it's nothing like that.' He looked quite upset at her opinion of his stepbrother. 'Rob isn't blackmailing me, Cadie, it's not that. It's just that he wants a crew for Sunday, he needs the practice for that race next month, and I almost always have crewed for him, except when Lida comes down, and I'd feel I was letting him down if I didn't go.'

'But it doesn't matter about letting me down?'

'I don't have to,' he assured her. 'We can both go with Rob.'

'Oh well,' she sighed resignedly, 'I suppose I should have known better than to try and get the better of Rob, shouldn't I?'

'Cadie, I'm sorry.'

'I know you are, Gordon, please don't worry about it too much. I understand.'

'And you'll – you'll come sailing instead on Sunday?'

'Oh no, indeed I won't,' she declared firmly. 'You can allow yourself to be ordered about to suit Rob, but I don't have to, and I've no intention of coming with you on Sunday.'

'But, Cadie—'

'It's no use, Gordon.' She set her mouth firmly, and there was a dark, determined look in her eyes. 'You go sailing with Rob, and I'll walk along to Dorly Point on my own.'

'But you can't!'

'Of course I can. It isn't very far, and I like walking.'

He looked at her for a moment, a rather lost and hopeless look on his good-looking face. 'Oh, damn Rob!' he exclaimed at last, and she felt the arm around her waist tighten in anger. A frustrated, futile anger because he knew she wanted him to come with her, as he had promised, and he hadn't the courage to defy Robert.

'I don't see why you couldn't go,' Dottie told her when she explained how her Sunday plans had been changed. 'It could be rather fun, love, and Rob's a very good sailor. I mean, you're not likely to end up in the sea or anything daft like that; you'd be quite safe. I don't see why you can't go.'

'Because I've no intention of letting Robert Dean have his own way all along the line,' Cadie declared firmly. 'It's time *some*body stood up to him. The man's an – an autocrat, an out-and-out despot, and I won't have my week-ends arranged to suit *his* pleasure!'

'Well, this one has been anyway,' Dottie pointed out, a small and rather annoyingly knowing smile on her round face, as if she found the whole situation rather amusing. Sometimes, Cadie thought, Dottie could be almost alarmingly like her employer.

'He may have got his own way with Gordon,' Cadie said, 'but he's not getting me aboard that – that blessed boat. I'd sooner drown first!'

'I wouldn't,' Dottie admitted with a grin. 'I'd make the most of my chances with a sailing boat, miles of empty sea and shore, and just me and a couple of dishy fellers. You don't know when you're well away, love.'

'I will not,' Cadie stated firmly, 'be shanghaied by Robert Dean. I'll sink his blessed boat first!'

Sunday was a beautiful day, despite Cadie's ardent prayers that it would be wet and much too squally to take out a boat. As she busied herself in the kitchen she thought ruefully that even the elements seemed to be on Robert's side. It was a perfect day for the picnic that she and Gordon had planned too, and she was going to have her picnic with or without Gordon.

She packed up some sandwiches and tea, put them all into a small holdall along with her swimsuit and her current reading, and set off along the coast road with a tilt of defiance to her chin for Gordon, Robert and anyone else who cared to call her stubborn and obstinate.

It was much warmer than even she had expected, and as Dorly Point came into view, she thanked heaven that she had thought to pack her swimsuit and a towel. A dip would soon cool her off after her walk.

The beach at Dorly Point was deserted and she sat down on the stretch of flat yellow sand thankfully. It was the work of minutes to shed her few clothes and put on a brief two-piece swimsuit, a flowery white cap covering her long hair.

The water was cool and refreshing and she swam quite a long way out before turning over on to her back and floating on the incoming tide. The sun in her eyes sent her back to shore at last, and she swam at a leisurely pace back to the spot where she had left her clothes, pulling off her cap and shaking out the silky blackness of her hair as she walked out of the water.

Somewhere here her clothes and bag should be, but as she looked about her, she realized with dismay what had happened. There was no sign of her clothes, and the holdall, only an empty beach and the water much higher up the beach than when she had left it.

'Oh no!'

She looked around her, blank-eyed and disbelieving that she could have been so careless. The tide had come up much faster and much further than she had estimated and she turned hastily just in time to see her dress, now a bedraggled rag, being sucked down in a lazily swirling tide. There was no sign of the holdall and, remembering its weight, she knew that it must already have been sunk without trace, along with her tea.

She stood for a moment or two, her thoughts chaotic, wondering how on earth she was to get back to

Dorly Creek dressed in nothing but a bikini. There was no other living soul in sight and she was disinclined to go up to where the road was and try to hitch a lift. For the moment she could think of nothing that was at all constructive.

If only – the words came into her mind and she dismissed them hastily. It was no use wishing that she had not come alone, it was done now, and she must think of some way out of her predicament that would cause her as little embarrassment as possible.

The sun glinted so brightly on the water and everything looked so wonderfully peaceful and calm that she could almost believe she was only dreaming this, and that everything would be all right once she woke up again.

For the moment her only instinct was to sit down, hugging her knees and stare at the sea, the eternal optimist in her waiting for something to turn up. Her Micawber streak, as Dottie always called it, only this time it was unlikely to produce anything helpful.

A small sailing craft appeared round the curve of the point, and she raised her chin from her folded hands hopefully. It might be better to be rescued from the sea than from land, and less embarrassing on the return journey – always, of course, providing that the occupants of the boat spotted her.

She hesitated only briefly, then gritted her teeth and got to her feet, waving both hands and hoping the sailors, whoever they were, did not think she was merely waving a greeting and pass by unheeding. There were two of them, she could see that much even from this distance, but whether they were men or women or both she could not yet tell.

Waving frantically now, she saw the little craft come nearer much more quickly than she expected, and at last an arm was raised in acknowledgment, but whether to greet her or signal understanding, she could not tell. What she did recognize with a sinking dismay, however, was that one of them was a definite blond and they were both male.

'Oh no!' Her heartfelt cry fell on the unheeding silence and she huddled down again, hugging her knees, wishing she had not taken the chance of hailing the first boat that came into sight.

The water was deep quite soon and they sailed quite close in, easily recognizable now, with Gordon cupping his hands to call out to her, his voice thinned by the distance and only just audible.

'Cadie! What's wrong?'

She got to her feet again, tiny and slender in her brief costume, on that deserted stretch of sand. 'I'm stranded!' she called. No more – he could draw his own conclusions from that.

There was silence for a second while that much was absorbed, then he cupped his hands to his mouth again. 'Can you swim out to us?'

She was tempted to say she wouldn't bother, but somehow she had to get home and at least she would be with someone she knew, although she hated to anticipate the amusement she knew it would afford Robert when he discovered what had happened. No doubt he would consider it a judgment on her for being stubborn and difficult and refusing to come with them in the first place.

She hesitated for so long that her rescuers had already taken things into their own hands and she saw the swift, graceful arch of a brown body curve into the water before she could shout agreement. It had to be Robert, of course, and she waited there for him to come out to her, wondering why it was him and not Gordon, as she would have preferred.

He came out of the water, tall and gleaming wet in a pair of brief swimming trunks, his blond hair darkened by the water so that he looked almost Indian with his all-over tan. His face, she noticed, was serious and not amused as she had expected, and she wondered if he was annoyed because his sailing had been interrupted.

He came straight to her and took her hands in his, the light grey eyes searching her face anxiously as he spoke. 'Cadie! Are you all right? What happened to you?'

She was annoyed to find her heart thudding frantically hard as he held her hands, and tried not to notice how undeniably attractive he looked. Exciting was a word that persisted even though she tried to dismiss it and she wished she had the will power to withdraw her hands instead of standing there as she was.

'Nothing's wrong,' she told him, in a small voice that made her sound as if she expected a reprimand for carelessness. 'I – I'm stranded here, that's all.'

'Stranded?' He looked at her curiously, taking in her lack of clothing, and the first glint of realization and laughter appeared in his eyes. 'Do you mean to say you could have swum out to us?' He gripped her hands harder, trying to make her look at him. 'You're not hurt?'

'No, I'm not hurt. Sorry to disappoint you.'

'You don't disappoint me, you little idiot, but why didn't you answer when Gordon asked if you could come out to us?'

'I – I was thinking.'

He raised appealing eyes to heaven. 'She was thinking,' he echoed. 'Will you tell me what happened here or do I have to shake it out of you?'

'I – I went for a swim, that's all, and when I came back—' she hesitated. This was where he would laugh at her. 'My – my things had gone.'

'Gone?'

She nodded miserably. 'The tide came in while I was swimming, I didn't realize how fast it came in.'

'You little dope!' He threw back his head and laughed loud enough for Gordon to hear him on the boat, and he came to the side and gazed across at them earnestly.

'Rob!'

Robert waved a hand at him. 'It's O.K.!' he called back, then looked down again at Cadie. 'So you got yourself stranded here with nothing but that brief bit of nonsense you're wearing and faced with a long walk home along the coast road.' He laughed again and Cadie clenched her hands, snatching them free of his hold. 'Oh, you *would* have caused a traffic jam, my sweet, wouldn't you?'

'It's not funny,' Cadie told him shortly, her cheeks flaming. 'And I'm not your sweet!'

'Aren't you?' His eyes held hers for a moment, then he swept his gaze over her from top to toe until she could have blushed all over. 'If it wasn't for Gordon's beady eye fixed on us from out there, I'd make the most of my chances, my sweet, you take my word for it.'

'Oh, why did it have to be you?' Cadie wailed in dismay. 'Why couldn't Gordon have come?'

'Because he didn't bring swimming trunks,' Robert explained with a grin. 'I did, and I'm glad I did now or I'd have missed this little pantomime.'

'I think you're – you're—'

He grabbed her hand tightly and drew her down towards the water, laughing softly as he pulled her along. 'Come on, you little water urchin, before you say something you'll be sorry for.'

'Wait – my hair!'

'What about it?' he asked, pausing in his stride but still keeping his hold on her hand.

'I must put my cap on first.'

'Right, put it on, but don't be too long or Gordon will think all sorts of things if we're too long, even though we're in full view. He's psychopathic when it comes to you and me.'

Cadie did not deign to answer that one, but pulled on her cap in disapproving silence, and walked into the water, Robert following, a smile on his face that made a mockery of her dignity.

Gordon reached over the side of the boat and helped her in, his good-looking face both anxious and curious, while Robert hauled himself over the side and flipped his wet hair from his forehead as he grinned at her.

'What happened, darling?' Gordon asked.

'I – I was stupid enough to leave my things too near the water,' Cadie told him, hating the way Robert was smiling as he listened to her explanation. 'The tide came in while I was swimming and they were washed away.'

'Oh, you poor love!' Gordon at least was sympathetic, and she could not resist a swift, I-told-you-so sort of glance at Robert, who laughed.

'Poor little idiot!' he retorted, and Gordon frowned.

'It could happen to anybody,' he said defensively. 'If you don't know the coast.'

'It *had* to happen to Cadie,' Robert declared with a broad grin that Cadie would love to have done something about. 'Everything happens to Cadie, doesn't it, my sweet?'

'Oh, don't be so damned superior!' Gordon told him shortly. 'And Cadie isn't *your* sweet.'

'O.K., O.K.,' Robert agreed soothingly. 'We've been through all that once.'

Gordon looked at him suspiciously. 'I can't see what you found to laugh at just now,' he informed him, and turned again to Cadie. 'Are you sure you're all right, darling? You're not hurt?'

'No, I'm perfectly all right, thanks, just – well, a bit conspicuously dressed for walking along the coast road back home. I didn't know quite what I should do for the best, then I decided it would be better to try and hail a boat rather than thumb a lift in a car.'

'That *would* have caused a riot on the Queen's highway!' Robert chuckled.

'It certainly would,' Gordon agreed wholeheartedly. 'I'm only glad it was us that came along first, Cadie. It could have been pretty risky even so.'

'Is that spelled r-i-s-q-u-é?' Robert inquired, and Gordon scowled at him discouragingly.

'I still don't think it's funny,' he told him. 'Anything could have happened. Not that you'd have cared, I expect, but I tremble to think what could have happened to her with *some* of the types there are about now.' He put a protective arm about Cadie's shoulders and hugged her consolingly.

'Well, we're the types she hailed, so there's nothing to worry about, is there?' Robert said a little impatiently. 'Except that the lady still hasn't any clothes to go home in. You're wearing a tee shirt you're not much use to her, but I'm wearing an ordinary shirt which will cover rather more of her, and she can have it with pleasure if she'd like to.'

'I—'

'If you're going to suggest that you have only to walk from the quay like that,' Robert interrupted. 'I wouldn't advise it. Dorly Creek's not ready for such pulchritude unadorned – you'll shock it to its puritan soul, walking about like that.'

'He's right,' Gordon admitted reluctantly, and Cadie was forced to agree that she would probably turn all heads if she walked home, even that short distance, as she was.

'You turn your back while I dry and make myself decent,' Robert told her, anticipating her acquiescence, 'and I'll give you my shirt. O.K?'

She nodded. 'Thank you.'

The shirt, of course, proved far too big for her, which was all to the good, she realized, for it came well down to her knees and looked almost like a shift with curved sides. A piece of rope knotted round her slim waist and the sleeves rolled up above her elbows and she looked far more respectable, if a little gamin. Robert grinned at her, a wicked gleam in his eyes as he winked.

'I must say it looks much better on you than it does on me,' he told her. 'You do *much* more for its contours.'

Cadie merely raised her chin and said nothing. It was bad enough having to wear his blessed shirt without his making remarks about it, that were obviously designed to annoy both Gordon and herself.

When they reached Dorly Creek and the quay, Cadie began to have qualms again about walking home in her unconventional garb, and she hung back when Robert offered a hand to help her ashore. Gordon was first ashore and tying up, that being part of his duties as crew, apparently.

'Come on,' Robert urged, and, when she still hesitated, lifted her bodily from the boat and stood her on the quay in front of him, his hands at her back, ignoring Gordon's black look.

'Thank you.' She could think of nothing more to say, and dared not look at him because she knew he was trying to flirt with her, with the express purpose of annoying Gordon, of course.

'Any time.' He squeezed her close to him for a second, long enough to make her gasp and for Gordon to pull at his arm to make him release her.

'I'll take you home, Cadie,' Gordon told her. 'Come on, darling.'

She went willingly enough, but she could not resist a brief look back as they walked along the quay. Robert still stood where they had left him and something in his stance seemed to Cadie like a challenge. He looked incredibly tall with his long legs in fitted trousers and his tanned torso naked because she was wearing his shirt. His blond head caught the sun and gleamed like gold, and she hastily put a hand to her face as he raised one hand in a salute that was almost mocking.

Gordon appeared not to notice her preoccupation, but seemed only glad to be free of his stepbrother, and hugged her to him, unaware that even at this distance Robert could prove a distraction.

CHAPTER SEVEN

'I'VE never felt so – so idiotic in my life,' Cadie told Dottie. 'And of course it would *have* to be Rob that came along. It wouldn't have been so bad if Gordon had been on his own, I wouldn't have minded so much, but you know what Rob's like.'

'Oh, I know what Rob's like! You must have looked cute in his shirt, though,' Dottie grinned. 'I'd love to have seen you.'

'Quite enough people saw me as it was,' Cadie retorted. 'That old colonel type at the corner house gave me a most peculiar look, especially when he noticed I had no shoes on.'

'Oh, of course you lost your shoes as well, didn't you?' Dottie sympathized. 'Did it hurt to walk, love?'

Cadie nodded. 'It did, that's why Gordon insisted on carrying me for most of the way, which rather defeated the object of trying to appear inconspicuous.'

'Mmm, I can imagine it would. How did Gordon take it?'

'My being stranded, you mean?'

'Yes. Was he all sympathy and kind words – he's rather a love, is our Gordon, and it was a marvellous opportunity for *him*, wasn't it?'

'He was very sweet,' Cadie told her, a little on the defensive. 'Much more understanding than Rob was.'

'He would be, at least on the surface,' Dottie said. 'He takes a rather different attitude towards things. Rob's inclined to treat everything as a joke. At least he appears to until you know him better, but he isn't always as flippant as he appears, Cadie, honestly.'

'No?'

'No. And he did lend you his shirt after all, didn't he?' Cadie allowed as much with a brief nod, and Dottie smiled. 'You see,' she told her knowingly. 'You should have gone sailing with them in the first place. Rob managed to get you aboard after all, didn't he?'

'Of course,' Cadie retorted. 'He *always* has to get his own way somehow or other. Even the elements are on his side.'

'Never mind, love,' Dottie consoled her. 'At least you were rescued by somebody you know. It would've been awful if you'd had to hitch-hike home along the coast road in your bikini. Not,' she added with a giggle, 'that you'd have had much difficulty getting a lift.'

'Sometimes,' Cadie told her sternly, 'I suspect that you caught something off Robert Dean when you were working for him. You used not to be like this, I'm sure.'

Facing Robert again after the incident was almost the worst part of the ordeal, for it was too much to expect that he would allow it to pass without comment when she returned to the office next morning.

Sure enough he caught her eye as he came into the room and solemnly lowered one lid. 'All present and correct after your battle with the high seas?' he asked, and Cadie nodded briefly.

'Yes, thank you.' She should, she supposed, make her thanks a little more effusive, since he had come to her rescue. 'I – I'm grateful to you for rescuing me,' she added, and he recognized her unwillingness with a wry grin.

'How're the feet?' he asked. 'I'm sorry we couldn't do anything about shoeing you, but even if we'd had a spare pair of sandals, they'd hardly have fitted your mini feet, would they?'

She rolled paper into her machine, hoping he would take the hint and drop the subject. 'Oh, you don't have to worry about me,' she said quietly. 'I was all right.'

'I wasn't exactly worried about you,' he informed her bluntly. 'But I wouldn't have liked you to hurt your feet. The quay isn't the softest surface to walk on.'

'But I didn't walk for very long. Gor—' She stopped herself there, too late, she realized, for he would probably find the idea of Gordon carrying her home as amusing as he seemed to find everything else to do with her mishap. 'I managed, thank you.'

'Gordon carried you,' he guessed, and laughed. She felt the colour in her cheeks as she kept her eyes determinedly lowered, but her silence was confirmation enough for him. 'So much for remaining inconspicuous,' he said.

'We weren't exactly conspicuous,' she objected. 'And anyway it was better than hurting my feet on the stones.'

'Of course it was,' he agreed. 'And people probably thought you'd had an accident and been drowned or something, anyway.'

'You talk as if Dorly Creek's as crowded as – as Blackpool in Wakes Week,' she told him. 'And I don't see why you have to worry. *You* weren't carrying me; Gordon was.'

He chuckled softly. 'Maybe I'm jealous,' he said.

'Oh, don't be so–' She stopped and bit her lip. 'No one much was about,' she added hastily.

'But somebody must surely have seen and noted young Mr. Charles walking along the quay with a half naked girl in his arms,' he insisted with a grin. 'And a girl wearing a man's shirt to boot. *That* must have raised a few eyebrows!'

'It did *not*,' Cadie denied.

'I'd have noticed it, especially as it was Gordon. No one would take so much notice of me, of course, they're used to having their blood pressures boosted when I'm around.'

'You sound proud of it!'

'Not really,' he grinned.

'Well, as it happens we saw only one man,' Cadie informed him shortly, wishing to heaven he would go and sit at his own desk instead of perching on the end of hers. 'At least only one who took any notice of us.'

'Old Mr. Smith-Plackett,' Robert guessed with a laugh, and she looked at him warily.

'I – I don't know who he was, although Gordon seemed to recognize him.'

'I can *guess* who it was,' he said. 'I thought he looked

as if he'd been shocked to the core of his righteous soul when he passed me on the quay.' He grinned delightedly as a new thought occurred to him. 'He probably thought you had nothing on at all under my shirt. He's a wicked-minded old devil under all that puritanical clap-trap, I've always said so.'

'Oh, you *would* think the worst!' Cadie retorted, and he laughed again.

'Old Smith-Plackett will, you can bank on it.'

'Is he very important?' She was worried now about Gordon being credited with an undeserved reputation for permissiveness.

Robert shrugged. 'Not important enough to worry about.'

'I mean will he gossip about Gordon? I'd hate him to be maligned because of me.'

He looked at her quizzically for a moment. 'You're doing Gordon an injustice if you think he'd care,' he told her.

'Just the same this – Mr. Smith-Plackett could make things unpleasant for him if he gossips.'

'Oh, he'll gossip,' Robert assured her airily. 'But I shouldn't let it worry you. He feels honour bound to report any what he calls goings on to all and sundry, but no one takes much notice of him. He's the leading light in the keep-Dorley-Creek-decent brigade.'

'He sounds dangerous.'

'Oh, he's not dangerous!' He dismissed her rather dramatic words with a casual hand. 'He's just a narrow-minded old man with not enough to do to pass the time. He's never approved of me,' he added, and smiled as if the idea pleased him.

Cadie looked at him briefly from under her lashes, curious about just what sort of a reputation he had among the local people. Good or bad, it was almost certain he wouldn't care either way.

'In your case he probably has good reason,' she hazarded rashly.

Robert leaned forward on his perch and lifted her chin sharply with one hand, so suddenly that she raised wide, startled eyes and saw an unexpected gleam of anger in his, as if he resented the jibe. 'You think so?' he demanded.

His fingers gripped her hard, digging into her jaw, so that she put up a hand to break his hold. 'You're hurting me!' she protested, and he laughed shortly, easing his grip but retaining his hold on her.

'You deserve it,' he told her. 'Making a crack like that.'

'But you said yourself that you put their blood pressure up,' she reminded him, and he laughed.

'So I did, but you don't have the right to agree with me. It's a subject you know little about.'

'I know what Dottie's told me!' That was rather unfair to Dottie, she realized too late, but it was said now and there was nothing she could do about it.

He pulled a face and winced. 'Ouch! Stabbed in the back by one of my faithful. Did Dottie really tell tales about me?'

Cadie looked uneasy. 'Not – not exactly,' she confessed, and he nodded.

'I thought so. You decided to read between the

lines, of course, and think the worst of me as usual, just for the hell of it.'

'I'm sorry.'

He looked a little surprised when she apologized, however grudgingly, and he held her for a moment longer, then laughed softly and bent his head to brush her mouth briefly in a kiss. 'So you should be,' he said.

Cadie said nothing for a moment, then she put her hands on the keys of the typewriter. 'I'd better get on with some work,' she told him.

'Coward!'

The accusation startled her and she looked up at him. 'I don't see—'

'You don't like it when you're made to feel like a real woman, do you, Cadie?' he asked softly.

'I don't know what you mean.'

'Oh yes, you do!'

She began to type, albeit clumsily because her fingers felt annoyingly weak and trembly, and she knew that when she got to the end of the line he would be in the way of the carriage if he did not move – and he didn't.

'If you'd—' she began, but instead of moving he slammed the carriage back across and kept a hand on it.

'I've never come across such a – a cantankerous, determinedly difficult female in my life,' he informed her quietly, but with an edge of annoyance on his voice. 'You just never yield an inch, do you?'

'I – I don't see how we can ever talk about anything,' Cadie said, wishing she could do something about the rapid and uneasy fluttering just under her ribs. 'We never see eye to eye about anything, and I doubt if we ever will.'

'You've made up your mind we shan't,' he retorted. 'After nearly four weeks of working for me, you still treat me as if I was some sort of dangerous monster, and I wish I knew why.'

'I do not!' Cadie denied indignantly. 'It's you that always starts these – these arguments, not me. I just want to do my job.'

'Oh, you little paragon of virtue!' he jeered, a glitter in his eyes of both anger and amusement, she recognized. 'Little injured innocent!'

'You don't have to be so – so nasty!'

'Don't I?' He looked down at her steadily and she could feel herself trembling, though what the emotion was that prompted it, she could not rightly guess. 'Do you know what you've done?' She shook her head dumbly, hastily lowering her eyes again. 'You've done more to shake my self-confidence in these three and a bit weeks than any woman I've ever known, and I don't like it. I don't like it one bit.'

'I don't see how,' she objected in a small voice that sounded far more meek than she had intended it should.

'I know you don't.'

'I – I work hard,' she insisted, refusing to recognize any other subject to discuss.

'You work hard!' He looked down at her, a curl on his lip. 'Oh yes, you work hard enough – especially at being an anti-Robert Dean feminist.'

'You have no right to say that!'

'I have every right,' he argued. 'You – you shatter me, the way you consistently refuse to—'

'To fall under the Dean charm?' Cadie hurled back, and he narrowed his eyes. 'In one breath you're proclaiming your – your innocence—'

'Heaven forbid!'

'Well, you reprimand me for suggesting old Mr. Whatsit has reason to frown on you and the next minute you're blaming me because I don't – I don't fall over myself to succumb to your charms.'

'I love your choice of phrase!' He smiled maliciously.

'Oh, you – I'm going to work, and ignore you!'

He shook his head, a faint disturbing smile crooking his mouth at one corner. 'You do that, my sweet, but don't try taking me on in a battle of words. Words are my business, remember.'

'I wasn't—'

He picked up one of her hands from the keys and held it in his own for a moment. 'You'd better just toe the line, Cadie O'Connor,' he said softly, 'or I'll throw you out on your pretty ear. Do you hear me?'

'Yes, I heard you.'

'Then remember it.'

Cadie clenched her hands. Unable to resort to thumping out her temper on the typewriter as she usually did at times like this, she had only one outlet for it, and he still sat, large and maddeningly calm on the end of her desk.

'In that case,' she told him, as firmly as she was able for a dismaying quaver in her voice, 'I'd better leave of my own volition before I'm sacked.'

He was silent for a moment, then he laughed and ran a caressing finger down her cheek. 'If that's the way you want it, my sweet, you leave,' he said softly.

She held his gaze for a moment, her bluff called, then hastily lowered her eyes. 'All right,' she said quietly, 'I will. Right now.'

'Oh no, you don't!' He stood up and put his hands on her desk, leaning forward so that his face was only inches from hers and his breath warm on her mouth when he spoke.

'But I—'

'Not on your life, you little paragon! You'll work out your month's notice.'

'But—'

'But nothing!' he retorted, his mouth crooked into a smile and his stubborn chin jutted adamantly. 'You'll do it according to the book, if you're determined to leave me.'

There was no way of denying that, she knew. He was entitled to a month's work from her before she left and he would hold her to it. She knew that too. There was no arguing with such downright obstinacy, and she felt her lower lip begin to tremble. She could have cried with temper, but such weakness was bound to be misconstrued; he must not see her cry, for heaven alone knew what her reaction would be if she was offered a comforting shoulder to cry on.

Gordon was appalled when she reported her decision to him that evening, and he looked almost ready to burst into tears himself at the idea of her leaving. 'But, darling, you can't,' he protested. 'Rob didn't mean it. I know him – he doesn't often lose his temper, but when he does he says things he doesn't mean.'

'It's what *I* mean in this instance,' Cadie told him. '*I* gave notice, Gordon, and I did mean it.'

'But tell him you didn't, please, Cadie!'

Cadie looked at him indignantly, her blue eyes dark, still shadowed with her anger for Robert. 'And let him think I'm backing down? No, Gordon, I can't, you know what he'd think as well as I do.'

'It doesn't *matter* what he thinks as long as you stay on here.'

'It does to me!'

'Oh, why do you have to be so stubborn?' He held her arms tightly and looked so unhappy about her going that, for the first time, she admitted to feeling regret.

'I – I'm sorry, Gordon.'

'You're as bad as Rob, you realize that, don't you?' he asked. 'You're just like him in a lot of different ways.'

'Oh, of course I'm not!'

'Of course you are!' he retorted, with unexpected sharpness. 'Neither of you will yield an inch once you've dug your heels in.'

It was unfortunate that he used Robert's words to scold her, for it did nothing to pacify her and she stuck out her chin firmly. 'If anybody's going to yield any inches in this particular instance,' she said, 'it's going to be Rob.'

Cadie still rankled under what she considered his injustice towards her, but Robert showed no signs of regret or relenting, in fact he behaved rather as if he expected things to go on as usual, something she could not bring herself to do.

He showed no sign of ill humour, nor did he attempt to make life any more difficult for her, and she was if anything made more uneasy by his friendly, outgoing manner. Mostly because she suspected him of plotting something, for whenever she caught him looking at her he was smiling in the most disturbing way. Although what it could be she had no idea.

She laundered the shirt he had loaned her and returned it a few days later, neatly ironed and parcelled. It was rather a surprise to find Mellida Dawson in the office on the Wednesday morning, and Cadie hesitated about handing over the parcel with the actress's sharp blue eyes turned on her, suspicious as ever.

One person at least, she thought, would be glad to see the last of her, although she had never given Mellida Dawson any reason to distrust her, except by going to the theatre with Robert just that one time. The other woman's antagonism towards her was based purely on speculation and the fact that she would probably have disliked any presentable girl who worked in close proximity to Robert.

She never quite knew what malicious imp of mischief made her walk straight across to Robert's desk and hand him the parcel, but she could not restrain the brief flick of satisfaction it gave her to see his companion frown.

'Good morning, Rob.' She handed him the parcel and moved across to her own desk without another word, but appalled to find that she was walking with a much more provocative swing to her hips than usual, and that Robert had not missed it.

'For me?' He looked at the brown paper bag, and smiled expectantly, either oblivious or uncaring of Mellida Dawson's frown.

'I'm just returning what's yours,' Cadie told him, and smiled. 'I didn't want it hanging around in the cottage in the circumstances.'

She could feel an almost dizzying sensation in her heart and wondered what on earth had possessed her to behave the way she had. Not that Robert would have been averse to the distraction, but for her own part she was already regretting it.

She heard the rattle of paper and knew he would be opening the parcel there and then, regardless of Mellida's hard, suspicious eyes and the tight little lines at the corners of her mouth.

'Ah yes, my shirt! I'd forgotten where it was.' He took it from its wrapping and examined it. 'I'm glad you've brought it back – and so beautifully laundered too. There's no end to your talents, my sweet.'

That embarrassing endearment fell on stony silence and she guessed he had used it with the express purpose of both embarrassing her and annoying Mellida. It had been too much hope that he would let her get away with her momentary rashness in behaving as she had.

Cadie said nothing, but Mellida took the bait obligingly. 'Darling,' she drawled, her sharp eyes flicking to Cadie and back to Robert, 'what on earth is Miss – er – doing with one of your shirts?'

'Returning it, as she said,' Robert informed her blandly.

'I can see that,' Mellida snapped, in no mood to be teased. 'What I want to know is how she came to have it in the first place.'

Robert lowered one eyelid, his eyes glinting wickedly when he looked across at Cadie. 'That,' he said, 'would be telling, wouldn't it, Cadie?'

'Rob!' Doubt edged the suddenly harsh voice, but she was already half believing it, Cadie thought, and wondered what she could possibly do to clarify the situation without going into too many details.

'Miss Dawson,' she began, but Mellida was in no mood to listen to anything from her.

'You don't have to explain,' she snapped. 'Spare me the details, please!' Her hands were working at her sides, Cadie noticed, and her eyes had an icy look. 'It's all too obvious how his clothes came to be at your cottage—'

'You're wrong!' Cadie declared hastily, her face a furious bright pink as she instinctively looked to Robert to explain.

'You – you little slut!' Mellida was not to be deprived of her big scene; she might almost have been enjoying it, Cadie thought wildly. 'You scheming, gold-digging little slut!'

'Lida! Stop it!' He was still finding it amusing, that much was evident in his eyes, but his voice was sharp and deep with anger too, and Mellida recognized it.

'How *could* you, Rob?' She looked at him, her eyes bright with anger, and with a promise of tears perhaps.

Robert sighed. 'Why must you always make such a mountain out of a molehill?' he asked.

'A molehill?' Mellida put one hand to her forehead, her expression almost tragic. 'You carry on with your secretary behind my back, and you expect me *not* to be upset about it?'

Robert raised his eyes to heaven, a piety which was ill suited to the present situation, Cadie felt. 'Oh, for heaven's sake don't be a fool, Lida!'

'A fool?' She was trembling as if she held herself in check only with difficulty, and Cadie felt bound to sympathize with her, at least in part, no matter what.

Mellida stood by his desk, her blonde head held back in a gesture of suffering dignity, her expression almost comically long-suffering, while Robert looked remarkably untouched by it all and sat twirling his pen between his fingers as if he was only waiting for her to finish before he went back to work.

'If that's all you have to say,' she told him, 'I won't stay any longer. And I'm really going this time, Rob, I shan't be back.'

The door slamming behind her made Cadie wince and left a long uneasy silence for a while. Robert still looked remarkably unconcerned and she was astounded at the way he could remain so calm after such a scene with what, according to Gordon and Dottie, was his most serious woman friend.

'I suppose,' she ventured after a few silent moments, 'I'm to blame for that in a way.'

The light grey eyes held her gaze and he smiled. 'Are you?'

'In – in a way.' It was hard to admit it, especially when he seemed not to care whether she took the blame or not. 'And – I'm sorry.'

'I don't see why you should be,' he told her bluntly. 'It wasn't your fault.'

'I know it wasn't,' she was stung to retort. 'But I suppose I gave you the idea of – of baiting her by returning that wretched shirt to you when I did. I should have kept it until she'd left.'

'You little liar,' he said, so matter-of-factly that she stared at him. 'You thoroughly enjoyed getting Lida's goat by tossing the cat among the pigeons, and you know it. And then swinging off across the office like a pint-sized Suzie Wong to crown it all. Don't look so righteously indignant and innocent, my sweet. You only began to get sorry when Lida walked out, before that you were relishing the idea of putting me firmly in my place by trying to embarrass me.' His grin showed that neither her attempts nor the result were worrying him unduly, and Cadie could think of nothing quite scathing enough to say, no matter how she tried.

'Don't worry about Lida, either,' he told her airily. 'She'll be back.'

CHAPTER EIGHT

GORDON sat with his hands clasped round his knees, his eyes gazing out at the sun sparkling on the water and the gulls swooping and drifting on the light breeze. It was a perfect morning and Cadie was thinking what a shame it was that tomorrow Gordon had promised to sail with Robert and she would have to spend Sunday on her own again.

'I feel incredibly lazy,' she said from her recumbent position beside him. Her own outlook was restricted to the high vault of blue summer sky with not a cloud in sight, her eyes lazily half closed as she breathed the almost sensual warmth of the turf and heather and stretched her limbs in the sun.

Gordon turned and looked at her over one shoulder, smiling at her. 'You *look* incredibly lazy too,' he told her, then frowned suddenly when he remembered how little time she had left. "You'll miss all this in London, Cadie.'

'I will.' She admitted it without hesitation, feeling again that twinge of regret that she was experiencing more and more lately.

He turned and rested on one elbow looking down at her, his good-looking face shadowed as he turned his back to the sun. 'I wish you wouldn't, Cadie.'

She sighed, turning her head in the warm-smelling grass, a small frown between her brows. 'You know I haven't any choice, Gordon, please don't start that all over again.'

'But you *have* got a choice,' he insisted. 'That's what makes it so – so damned silly. You could back down, or Rob could, but both of you are so blasted stubborn that you'll neither of you give in.'

Even lying flat on her back she managed to stick out her chin. 'If he wants me to stay he has only to say so,' she told him.

'But you know he won't.'

'And neither will I.'

He traced the outline of her mouth with a gentle finger, hesitant and uncertain of the reception he would get. 'I could,' he ventured, and Cadie looked at him curiously.

'You could?'

'I could let Rob know that you really want to change your mind, but you're too stubborn to do so.'

'He already knows that,' Cadie retorted. 'And if you say anything to him that sounds even remotely like a peace move on my behalf, Gordon, I'll never forgive you!'

'But *why*?' Gordon asked, exasperated. 'You want to stay here, and yet you'll do nothing about healing the breach between you and Rob.'

'Why should it be me? Why not him?' Cadie demanded. 'He was ready enough to take me up when I said I was leaving, so why shouldn't he make the first move now?'

'Oh – because he's who he is, that's why,' Gordon said. 'You know Rob, he'll never change his mind, or at least he'll never let you know he has, but I know he doesn't want you to leave.'

Cadie turned her head and looked at him through narrowed eyes. 'How do you know that?'

He shrugged. 'I just know.'

'Maybe wishful thinking on your part, more likely,' Cadie laughed. 'Besides,' she added lifting a hand to touch his face, 'you'd do almost anything to get *your* own way too, wouldn't you?'

'I would in this instance,' he agreed. He was silent for a moment, leaning above her, seeking some way to make her see things his way. 'You know,' he said at last, 'a man doesn't like backing down to a woman. It – it isn't the natural order of things.'

Cadie glared up at him unbelievingly. 'You too!' she exclaimed. 'You've been listening to Robert too much, now you've got that – that nasty, mean sex discrimination thing all worked out to your own advantage.' She sat up, her mouth pouting reproach, tossing back the long mane of her hair in a gesture of defiance. 'Well, it won't work – not with me, it won't!'

Gordon took her arms and turned her round to face him, his expression more determined than she had ever seen it. 'All I know is that I love you,' he told her, 'and that if you and Rob go on with this ridiculous feud, I'll lose you. I've *got* to do something about it.'

'Well, there's nothing you can do,' she said, feeling strangely elated at the forcefulness of his declaration. 'Unless you can make Rob back down, and I can't see *that* happening either.'

'Marry me!'

Cadie blinked at him for a moment uncomprehendingly. 'You—'

He pulled her closer to him, his face solemn and earnest. 'If you marry me, you'll *have* to stay here!'

'Oh, Gordon, I can't!'

'I don't see why not,' he said, looking a little deflated at her adamant refusal.

'But of course I can't.' She smiled suddenly, unwilling to hurt him. 'It isn't that I don't like you, Gordon, you know that, but liking isn't enough reason to marry you.'

'I hoped you felt a bit more than like for me,' he said. 'I can see I was wrong.'

'But it's too soon, Gordon, much too soon.' She looked up at him anxious not to alienate him with her refusal, but quite sure she was right to refuse him in the circumstances. 'Please don't be hurt or angry – I do like you very much.'

He laughed shortly, his hands holding her either side of her head, his fingers caressing her neck. 'Rob says I fall in love too easily, doesn't he?' he said. 'But I really mean it this time, Cadie.'

'I wish I was as sure how I felt.'

'You're not sure?' he seemed immoderately pleased with that.

'I – I think I could fall in love with you, in time,' she told him, and wondered how rash she was being in confessing so much. 'But I just don't know at the moment, Gordon, and I can't commit myself to anything until I do.'

'Then I'll wait.'

She made no protest when he kissed her, long and

lingeringly on her mouth, and held her close to him, his face buried in her hair. 'Give me more time,' she whispered against his chest. 'I need time, Gordon.'

It would be quite easy to fall in love with him, she knew, if she allowed herself to. He had all the requisite qualities, enough for any girl. He was good-looking, charming and quite wealthy, and no doubt Dottie would tell her she was just being stubborn in not accepting him here and now. If he lacked a certain exciting quality in his personality, it was perhaps all to the good. For, while she admitted that Robert could be a much more exciting proposition, no girl in her right mind would want to face the rest of her life with a man like Robert Dean.

'Darling – what are you thinking about?' He kissed her again, and she smiled.

'About spending the rest of my life up here in the sunshine,' she told him. 'And never have to lift a finger to a typewriter again.'

'I can't promise the first,' he said, 'but the second you can have, if you marry me.'

She laughed softly, her arms round his neck. 'A life of leisure?' she said. 'I'm not sure I could cope with that, Gordon.'

'Leisure and pleasure,' he told her, kissing her between each word. 'You'd love it, darling. No more coping with Rob's moods, just think of it.'

She laughed again, but a little uncertainly as she gazed over his shoulder at the placid summer scene behind him. It was a thought that constantly haunted her during these waiting days, that when she went it would be Rob she missed most, but she dismissed it hastily with a shake of her head, looking up at Gordon's sober, good-looking face and wondering why she did not say 'yes' to him right now. For surely it was a chance she should grasp with both hands.

'I told you she'd be back,' Dottie informed Cadie when she went to see her on Sunday morning and reported that Gordon was unexpectedly free because Mellida Dawson had arrived.

'Rob told me so, too,' Cadie retorted. 'You two seem to share the same clairvoyance.'

'Two great minds,' Dottie agreed. 'But anyone could have guessed she'd come back before very long, Cadie. She always does.'

'And no doubt he's as smug as a cat that's been at the cream,' Cadie guessed. 'Oh, I wish she'd stayed away this time, just to show him!'

Dottie laughed, 'You *do* sound vicious, love!'

'I'm not vicious at all,' Cadie denied. 'But if only he wasn't always so blessed right all the time, he'd be a bit more bearable.'

'I reckon you'll miss your fights with him,' Dottie declared, and grinned when Cadie looked at her suspiciously. 'You *do* quite enjoy having a go at him, don't you?' she said.

'Oh, you're as bad as he is,' Cadie informed her defensively. 'He's implied that more than once.'

'Well, there you are – he's always right, you've just said so,' Dottie crowed triumphantly.

'Not this time!'

Dottie looked at her speculatively for a moment. 'Oh well,' she said, 'you'll miss Gordon anyway. You like him, don't you?'

Cadie nodded, willing enough to admit. 'I like him a lot,' she admitted. 'But not enough to marry him.'

Dottie looked at her curiously. 'Has he asked you?'

'Yes.'

'Oh, Cadie love, how marvellous!' She took her hands and tried to read her own interpretation into Cadie's reluctance. 'But you're playing hard to get?'

'No. No, of course not, Dottie, I wouldn't do that, but – well, I just don't feel sure enough of myself yet to marry him, that's all.'

'And you've said no?'

'I've said no.'

'Oh, dear,' Dottie wailed in comic dismay, 'what *am* I going to do with you?'

'Give me up as a bad job,' Cadie suggested with a short laugh, but Dottie shook her head determinedly.

'Never,' she said. 'You're destined for the altar, my girl, no matter how much you kick at the traces. Somebody'll take you in hand one of these days, and when he does you'll wonder why you didn't give in gracefully before.'

Gordon had promised they should go over to Dorfleet again one Saturday night before she left, and Cadie was really looking forward to it. Not that she had developed gambling fever since her one previous visit, but the idea of an evening dining, dancing and visiting the club again fitted her rather restless mood.

Already two weeks of her month's notice had gone and she was genuinely regretting that rash moment that had put her in the position where she must either beg forgiveness of Robert or leave the peaceful and pleasant life at Dorly Creek. At times, she admitted, she was tempted to eat humble pie and ask Robert if she could stay on, but then he would do or say something that infuriated her and she would rather have died than back down.

Both Gordon and Dottie, she felt sure, expected her to weaken before her time was up, but she had so far resisted all their blandishments as well as her own inclinations. It was unfair, she decided, to expect *her* to be the one to capitulate.

She was ready in good time for her date with Gordon, her new yellow dress making her look and feel rather exotic. She had plaited her hair into one thick braid which she wore over her left shoulder, and with a jewelled slide just above her left ear.

Taking one more critical look in the mirror, she started almost guiltily when the door-knocker rat-tatted its summons, and went to answer it, picking up her bag on the way.

She already wore a welcoming smile before she realized that it wasn't Gordon on the doorstep, but Robert, and she hastily dismissed the smile as she looked at him. For a second she had the sickening thought that something had happened to Gordon, but Robert was smiling and, no matter what she thought of him, she knew he would not find any accident to his stepbrother amusing.

He pursed his lips in a silent whistle of appreciation and leaned one hand on the lintel of the door while he swept a long, slow gaze over her from head to toe. 'No wonder Gordon was so mad about not coming,' he said, without preliminary greeting.

'Not – not coming?' She felt the cold sensation of bitter disappointment at the prospect of a ruined evening, especially when she had so looked forward to it.

'He's had to go to town suddenly,' he told her. 'A sudden panic about that play. Sorry about it, but there you are.'

Cadie looked at him suspiciously for a moment, her disappointment making her less than fair. '*You* sent him,' she accused, and he shook his head.

'Honest – I didn't.'

'Then why haven't you gone?' she demanded. 'It's your play.'

He looked at her steadily for a moment and she could feel the increased rate of her heart beat as she clutched her bag in both hands. 'It's his business to handle snags like that,' he told her quietly. 'He's my agent, etc., and it's what I pay him for.'

She shook her head slowly, realizing he was right, but hating to see her lovely evening coming to nothing. She felt very much like crying, which would be utterly ridiculous, of course, and would probably make him jeer at her for being a baby.

'I'm – I'm sorry,' she said instead. 'I was just disappointed, that's all.'

'You won't accept second best?'

He was looking at her, and if she had not known him better, she would have sworn there was a plea somewhere behind the look of gentle amusement in his eyes.

'Second best? You mean—'

'I mean I put on my best bib and tucker in the hope that you'd come with me instead.'

'You're—'

'Second best,' he said with a wry smile.

She looked at him for a moment, her mind racing on all the many reasons why he should be doing this, just because Gordon had been obliged to let her down at the last minute. 'You not seeing—' She bit her lip on the near-indiscretion, and saw his mouth crook into a smile.

'I'm not seeing anyone except you,' he told her. 'I promised Gordon I'd phone you when he had to dash off, but then I decided that you might just settle for a stand-in, and I came round here instead.'

'Thank you.'

'Is that a dismissal thank-you?'

'No. No, of course not. I'd – I'd like to come with you, please. I'm not in the mood for staying home. I was looking forward to this evening.'

'Then I'll do my best not to disappoint you.' He held out a hand to her. 'Shall we go?'

As they drove along the coast road to Dorfleet Cadie was reminded of the last time she had spent an evening in Robert's company, and hoped the outcome this time would be less disturbing. It was unlikely that they would bump into Mellida Dawson as they had done in town, but the thought refused to be dismissed and she was more than usually quiet as they drove along.

Robert glanced at her over his shoulder, a faint smile on his lips when he saw her solemn expression. 'Are you always as quiet as this?' he asked. 'Or is it reserved for me?'

Cadie turned her head, studying the strong, craggy features for a moment before she answered. 'I just couldn't think of anything to say,' she told him at last, and he laughed softly.

'What an admission to make!' he teased. 'Do I cramp your style, my sweet?'

'Rob, I – I wish you wouldn't use that – that name.'

'My sweet?' He sounded surprised, then chuckled again. 'Does it smack too much of male superiority?' he asked.

'Of male condescension!' she retorted, and bit on her lip hard. She had been determined not to argue with him and already she had weakened, or to be more accurate, allowed herself to be weakened. 'Please, Rob.' She clenched her hands and sought to still the rapid beat of her heart. 'I don't want to argue with you.'

He did not look at her, but one hand reached over and took hers, raising it briefly to his lips. 'Then don't, my sweet,' he said softly. 'And I promise I won't tease you. O.K.?'

'O.K.'

They were shown to a corner table in the same restaurant she had visited with Gordon, and Robert smiled wryly when heads turned in their direction. 'Coming out with you is good for my self-confidence,' he told her as they sat waiting for their meal, and Cadie smiled.

'I seem to remember,' she said softly, 'that you accused me of undermining your self-confidence, once upon a time.'

'So I did.' His light eyes glittered at her in the tanned face and she was surprised to find herself holding his gaze instead of lowering her eyes as she always did instinctively.

'I shouldn't remind you,' she said, with pseudo-meekness. 'I promised not to say anything to provoke an argument.'

'*I* promised,' he corrected her with a smile. 'You didn't commit yourself either way.'

'Sauce for the goose,' Cadie quoted solemnly, 'is sauce for the gander.'

'A very fair adage,' he declared, his eyes twinkling, 'but one used only one way by your sex as a rule.'

Cadie sighed. 'There you go again,' she said. 'That old, old prejudice.'

'Prejudice?' He raised a doubtful brow. 'I think we come down to basic facts here, Cadie. Men have always taken the dominant role in society, and I don't think it's a tradition it's going to be very easy to overthrow.'

'Overthrowing tradition has nothing to do with it,' she argued, forgetting her vow. 'It's the – the condescension we have to put up with. How would you like it if I called *you* my sweet?'

He laughed. 'I'd probably lap it up,' he told her. 'Although I'd rather you used something a bit less feminine.'

'There you are, you see!' Cadie said triumphantly. 'Even endearments come in different sexes.'

'Not all of them,' he denied with a grin. 'How about darling and sweetheart, they're pretty unisexual, aren't they?' He held her gaze. 'Why not try one of those for size?' he suggested quietly.

She could feel the warm colour in her cheeks and was very conscious of the wine waiter's eye as he proffered a bottle of Chablis for Robert's approval. Robert's gaze challenged her to continue the conversation while the man was there, but she determinedly kept her eyes lowered and refused to say anything.

The waiter moved discreetly away and a hand pushed her full wine glass nearer to her hand. 'Have a drink, darling, you'll feel better.'

'Rob—'

'There's nothing condescending about that,' he told her. 'And this is a very good wine.'

Cadie looked at him for a second, in silence, then reached for her glass and sipped the smooth sweetness of the wine. 'Very good,' she agreed, and caught his eye. Why that should have been her undoing she could not have said, but before she realized it, she was laughing. There was no reason for her laughter that she could think of, only the sudden and inexplicable excitement that stirred in her and some deep, unfathomable expression in Robert's eyes as he looked at her.

'To you,' he said softly, raising his glass. 'May you always look as beautiful as you do now.'

'Skoal!' She raised her own glass and drank deeply. 'I feel like getting a little high,' she informed him solemnly, 'so I probably will.'

Robert laughed, a deep, warm sound that trickled along her spine like an icy finger and made her shiver. 'Why not, if that's your pleasure?' he said. 'I'm driving.'

They managed to get through the first two courses of the meal without even a sharp word between them, and Cadie smiled when a delicious-looking confection of fruit, cream and meringue was put in front of her. 'It looks gorgeous,' she said, spoon poised. 'It's almost a shame to spoil it.'

'It's a special favourite of mine,' Robert confessed. 'And when I come here I always indulge myself.'

'Always?' She sampled the sweet and nodded approval. 'It *is* good. What is it?'

He grinned at her meaningly. 'Crême Robert.'

'Oh?' She looked down at her sweet curiously. 'In your honour?'

'Not exactly,' he admitted. 'Although I used to think so.' He laughed. 'Now you're more curious than ever, aren't you?'

'Of course.'

'Well, it's a long story, but briefly, when I was a child I had a French nurse and she used to spoil me silly, so I've been told. She used to pamper me with this because I was so fond of it and because it had the same name as I had. I discovered after I came here that the same sweet was on the menu, and after asking about it, found that my old nurse's nephew was the chef here. Of course I didn't get brandy in mine,' he added, and she laughed.

'I should hope not, but it's delicious.'

He grinned, spooning up another mouthful. 'I remember, years ago,' he said, 'Gordon hurled a whole dishful of it at me.'

'Oh?' She looked at him curiously, and a little suspiciously. 'Why?'

He shrugged. 'Probably because of its name,' he said simply.

Cadie said nothing for the moment, sensing the inevitable if she attempted to defend Gordon, and she was enjoying herself too much at the moment to spoil it all. 'It must have made quite a mess,' was all she said.

'Oh, it did, and I was dressed to take out a rather special girl too, which could have had something to do with it.'

'Oh, I see.'

'Do you, Cadie?' He held her gaze, his eyes serious despite the faint smile he wore. 'I'm just trying to warn you,' he said. 'That girl was Gordon's too, and he's likely to be pretty mad when he knows you've been here with me tonight. Will you mind?'

She ate the last of the cream from the shallow dish and put down her spoon carefully before she replied. 'I don't think he'll mind in the circumstances,' she told him, only half believing it herself.

He eyed her for a minute, speculatively. 'You don't appear to know my stepbrother very well,' he said.

'I think I do.' She raised her eyes, prompted by heaven knew what. 'He's asked me to marry him.'

Robert nodded, twisting the stem of his wine glass between restless fingers. 'I know,' he said. 'He told us.'

'Did – did he tell you that I—'

'He said you'd asked for more time, I think was the phrase,' he said, and added with a wry smile, 'He was unusually forthcoming about it. I really think he means it with you.'

'With me?' She had an uneasy feeling in her heart that the good part of the evening was over.

Robert was not looking at her, and that was un-characteristic of him. 'Of course with you,' he said, and so obviously trying to avoid explaining something he had said and now regretted.

'Rob.' She put out a hand and touched him, and he raised his eyes and looked at her steadily.

'He loves you, Cadie.'

'I – I think he does, at least—' She hesitated to voice her doubts, but something drove her on and she found the small light contact with him almost a comfort. 'I'd like to know,' she said. 'There've been others, haven't there?'

He looked down at his wine glass again and he was so very uncertain that she could scarcely believe it was Robert she was looking at. 'There have been others,' he said at last.

'You told me so right at the beginning,' she reminded him in a small voice. 'You said – you said he falls in love too easily, and he admits it, too.'

'Once—' He shrugged hastily. 'Oh well, that's ancient history now, and as I said, you're very different.'

Cadie remembered the whip he had cracked over Gordon to get him to break a date with her and crew for him. He had helped Gordon out of one or two scrapes, so Gordon had said, but it had not occurred to her to question the kind of scrapes he had referred to.

'Rob, please tell me. Has he – has he asked someone else to marry him? I mean,' she added hastily, 'in the past, of course.'

He nodded, still not looking at her, as if the blame was his and not Gordon's. 'In the past,' he said.

'More than once?'

'More than once.' He reached out and took her hand, holding it tightly in both his own, his eyes darker and more serious than she had ever seen them. 'But I'm sure he means what he says with you, Cadie, I'm sure he does.'

'He – he says he means it,' Cadie told him, 'and I think he does.' She smiled at him wryly, seeking to lift the air of solemnity that had settled on them. 'But that *could* just be my feminine conceit, of course,' she added, and he squeezed the hand that he held before releasing it.

'If he lets *you* down,' he said softly, 'I'll personally knock his stupid head off for him.'

It was quite late when they left the gambling club, and Cadie was the richer by nearly twenty pounds. The mere fact of winning at all had been exciting enough; the amount had astounded her. To be able to make so much in such a little time was almost incredible, and how Robert had laughed at her excitement.

They drove home along the coast road, and Cadie leaned back in her seat, her head resting on the back of it, her eyes half closed, very tired but very happy too. Even Gordon was forgotten for the moment and she gave no thought to the fact that she would be leaving Dorly Creek in a very short time.

'Tired?' Robert smiled at her over his shoulder, and she shook her head.

'Not really,' she said. 'I've had a wonderful time.'

'All that lovely money,' he teased, and she laughed.

'All that lovely money.'

'You mercenary little devil!'

'No, I'm not,' she objected, but mildly. 'But it's nearly a week's salary to me, you know, and just for – for putting a bit of plastic on the right number at the right time – well, it seems a bit unfair somehow.'

'You're not thinking of giving up secretarial work to become a full-time gambler, are you?'

'Good lord, no!' She looked at him through a thick fringe of black lashes. 'Suppose I lost?'

His laughter evoked a response from her, and she studied him through half closed eyes for several minutes, until he turned his head and looked at her, his smile showing white against the darkness of his face.

'You were talking of getting high,' he reminded her. '*Are* you?'

Cadie considered for a moment or two. Certainly something was giving a lift to her spirits, and she had not felt so lighthearted for a very long time, but she did not remember drinking very much wine. 'I think I must be,' she said at last. 'At least I feel all sort of nice and zizzy and my pulse is a bit fast. Yes – I *must* be high.'

'Or something,' Robert murmured softly, and laughed as he turned a corner.

'I shall miss Dorly Creek,' Cadie said, suddenly remembering, and wishing she hadn't.

'Dorly Creek will miss you.' He sounded very serious about it and she looked at the craggy, dark profile under its thatch of blond hair. Suddenly it wasn't so easy to be stubborn any more, and she wanted to tell him that she hadn't really meant it when she told him she would leave. If only – she bit her lower lip and turned her head away, determined not to be influenced by what could only be a momentary weakness.

They said nothing more until they neared the top of the narrow little lane leading down to her cottage, then she sat up suddenly and looked at him. 'You can drop me off here,' she said. 'There's no need for you to negotiate this narrow lane in the dark.'

'Nonsense!' he laughed, turning the corner into the lane. 'You're the one who's high, not me.'

'But, Rob—'

'It's done,' he said, and a few moments later braked to a halt outside her little cottage.

She did not move for a second, then some small sudden movement of his made her reach for the door handle, and she felt a tight, choking sensation in her throat as her heart thudded like a wild thing at her ribs. 'Goodnight, Robert.'

His hand covered hers on the door handle until she relinquished her hold, then slid down to her waist and pulled her across the seat towards him. There was a tense strength in the arms that held her and she closed her eyes, unprotesting, when his mouth found hers and set her heart pounding even faster until she was dizzy with its clamour.

She turned in the narrow confines of the seat and slid her arms round his neck, pressing closer until she could feel the steady, urgent beat of his heart too, and her fingers held tight to the thick blond hair that grew on his neck.

She lay for a moment against his chest, his face buried in the softness of her hair, his arms tight around her, then, suddenly and without warning, he released her and held her at arm's length, his eyes quizzical although they were dark in the dim light that reached them from the car headlights and it was difficult to judge their meaning.

'Don't get the stand-in used to the perks of the leading man,' he told her lightly. 'It could be dangerous.'

'Rob!' She wished she could see his face more clearly and determine his expression, but there was no betraying gleam of white, so he was not smiling.

'I stood in for Gordon,' he reminded her. 'And you *are* a little high, my sweet.' He got out of the car and came round to open her door, evidently determined to let it go no further. Considering Gordon's feelings, she thought, and knew she should have done so too, but she found it difficult at the moment. He helped her from the car and held on to her hand as they walked to the cottage door. 'You're a very heady wine, Cadie O'Connor,' he said softly, 'and a man could easily get carried away.'

He took her key from her unresisting fingers and unlocked the door, switching on the light just inside, then dropping the key into her hand again. Goodnight, Cadie.'

She stood for a moment in the lighted doorway, uncertain and feeling rather sad suddenly. 'Goodnight, Rob.' She raised her eyes and met his briefly, then turned into the tiny hall.

She felt the pressure of his lips lightly on hers and then the door slammed shut, but she was unsure whether she had done it herself or if he had. She leaned against it for a moment, her legs feeling ridiculously weak and shaky so that she put her hands behind her to support herself and closed her eyes.

Why, she thought wildly, hadn't he asked her to stay on?

CHAPTER NINE

'You weren't there,' Gordon accused. 'I came round as soon as I got back last night. I know it was late, but – well, I wanted to see you. To explain personally why I couldn't keep our date last night, and you weren't even there.'

'I'm sorry you had a wasted journey, Gordon.' Cadie tried not to sound impatient, but it was difficult when he seemed so bent on making a major issue of it.

She could not have been expected to foresee his earlier than expected return from London and it was quite unreasonable of him to behave as if he thought she could. He was looking at her as if she had committed some dastardly crime instead of having an evening out, but she refused to feel guilty about it.

'I couldn't believe it when I realized you'd gone off with Rob instead,' he went on. 'Why, Cadie?'

She hugged her knees and shrugged. They had walked up to their favourite spot on the headland in almost complete silence, and he had waited until they were sitting side by side on the warm springy turf overlooking the sea, before he had mentioned last night at all.

'I was all ready to go out,' she told him. 'Wearing my new dress and – and feeling rather excited about our evening out. I didn't *want* to stay in after that, it would have been an awful anti-climax.'

'Yes, yes, I realize that, but I couldn't help it. There was nothing I could do to get out of going. These sudden snags are a damned nuisance and it's always me that has to cope with them. I *did* ask Rob to let you know as soon as he could.'

'And he did.'

'He could have rung you,' Gordon said. 'Instead he had to come round in person, of course. That's typical of him.'

'Well, I'm *glad* he did,' Cadie declared firmly. 'I didn't feel like staying in on my own especially after all the trouble I'd gone to getting ready.'

'You could have gone to Dottie's.'

'Oh, I know I could!' She allowed her exasperation to show at last and he looked rather surprised. 'But I didn't want to sit at home at Dottie's either, and Rob asked me to go with him instead, so I did.'

'Well, I just don't understand you,' he complained. 'You're running this – this idiotic feud with him, and yet you don't think twice about going out with him for the whole evening.'

'He's good company, no matter what I think of him in other directions.'

'I'm glad to hear it!'

She looked at him, beginning to feel irritated by his stubborn ill humour. 'Oh, Gordon, can't you forget about it?' she said. 'I don't see why you have to make quite so much fuss about an innocent evening out.'

'Don't you?' He looked at her moodily over his shoulder. 'I know Rob better than you do.'

She could not resist a smile at the coincidence that made him choose the same words Robert had used. 'And Rob says *he* knows *you* better than I do.'

'Oh?'

'And I think you're both wrong. You're neither of you what you appear to be on first acquaintance.'

He looked at her again, unhappily, it seemed. 'You liked me when we first met,' he said, and Cadie smiled, covering her hand over his.

'I still like you,' she told him. 'I like you a lot, Gordon, you know that, but – but I don't like you treating me as if I've no right to speak to anyone else, or go out with anyone else. You don't own me.'

'I'm sorry.'

'Oh, Gordon!' She tucked her arm through his and laid her head on his shoulder. 'There's only two more weeks until I leave Dorly Creek,' she said. 'I don't want to quarrel with you.'

He turned round and pulled her to him, burying his face in her hair, so that his voice was muffled when he spoke. 'Cadie! Oh, Cadie, please marry me.' He kissed her and there was an urgency in his kiss that she responded to for a moment, and she put her arms round his neck. But then she recalled Robert's kiss of last night and a skip of panic touched her heart so suddenly that she shook her head and pulled away from him.

'I – I can't, Gordon.'

'Can't?' He held her tight enough to make her short-breathed and she tried to ease his hold on her.

'I've told you why, Gordon. If there was more time I

think it might be different, but there isn't. I have to go in two weeks' time, I have no choice.'

'You *have*,' he insisted. 'You could ask Rob to keep you on, you know he *would*, if you asked him.'

It was such a temptation, she thought. Of course Robert would let her stay on if she asked him, but she was not at all sure that staying on would solve anything. Gordon would read into her surrender, a desire to stay near him, but heaven knew what Robert would read into it.

She thought of that kiss again, and the way Robert had joked about his being only a stand-in, but he was not the type of man to stand in for anyone, certainly not more than once, and there had been something more in that kiss last night than merely the lighthearted end to an evening out. A promise, she thought as her heart thudded again at her ribs, a promise of something she dared not even think about.

'I – I can't ask him, Gordon.'

He looked at her in silence for a moment, then lifted her chin with one hand. 'Not even after last night?' he asked quietly, and Cadie raised startled eyes.

Surely Robert wouldn't have – but no, he wouldn't have told Gordon anything other than that he had taken her out for the evening. It had been he, after all, who had remembered Gordon and been strong-willed enough to break off so suddenly when she had been too involved to care. He would not have told Gordon anything else – he was too fond of his stepbrother for that.

'Last night had no effect on the matter at all,' she

told him. 'It wasn't even mentioned.'

'Do you mean—'

'I mean there was no sign of capitulation on either side,' she said, ignoring her own temptation on the way home.

'You stubborn, unyielding, blockheaded pair,' Gordon declared exasperatedly, then kissed her again with a fierce determination. 'If neither of you will do anything about it, I'll make my own plans,' he told her, 'whether you like it or not.'

'I don't know what he's up to,' Cadie confessed to Dottie a couple of evenings later. 'I wish I did.'

'You think he's making peace moves with Rob?' Dottie asked, and Cadie shrugged. 'It wouldn't be a bad thing, love.'

'I'm not so sure.' Cadie studied her clasped hands, wishing Dottie was not watching her with that knowing expression on her face.

'You mean you don't want to stay on here?'

'Yes. Yes, of course I do, but—' She shrugged again, hating the feeling of indecision. 'I just don't know what to do for the best, that's all, Dottie.'

'If you take my advice,' Dottie told her, 'and I don't for one minute expect you to do any such thing, you'll turn on all your feminine charm and ask Rob to let you stay on.'

'I – I don't think I can, Dottie.'

'Oh, nonsense, of course you can,' Dottie retorted, seeing her obvious weakening. 'Go on, love, go all sweet and reproachful and see what effect it has on him. I know Rob, he'll be only too glad to lay out the red carpet for you. He's a darling when it comes to accepting apologies.'

'He'd crow over me,' Cadie guessed gloomily. 'I know he would, and then I'd probably throw everything at him that I could lay my hands on.'

'He wouldn't,' Dottie assured her. 'Honestly he wouldn't, Cadie. You try and see.'

'Gordon wants me to.'

'He would,' Dottie said with a grin. 'He wants you here, and he's pretty good at getting his own way too.'

Cadie look at her and smiled ruefully. 'Everyone, it seems,' she said, 'wants me to stay on. I think I'm flattered.'

'So ask Rob, hmm?'

Cadie sighed deeply. 'All right,' she agreed. 'I'll ask him in the morning, only I can't promise how submissive I'll feel, and if he *does* act the magnanimous despot I'll hit him – I swear I will!'

'If he does,' Dottie laughed, 'he'll deserve it.'

Cadie arrived at work rather earlier than usual the following morning, and still in two minds whether to speak to Robert about staying on, as she had more or less promised Dottie she would do. She could not imagine, either, what had prompted her to dress with extra care this morning, unless Dottie's words about turning on her feminine charm had unconsciously had some effect.

The deep sea-green dress, long-sleeved and slimly

cut, gave her an exotic but dainty look and suited her colouring well. She smoothed a hand over her hair nervously as she sat down at her desk and already wished she had not been so rash as to promise Dottie she would raise the subject of staying on.

She had barely time to roll a sheet of paper into the machine, however, before the door opened to admit Robert, and she looked almost startled when he came in. He too was earlier than usual though heaven knew what his reason was. As usual he smiled across at her and said 'good morning', but she thought there was some small, indefinable difference in his manner this morning. Unless, of course, she was influenced by her own nervousness.

He sat down at his desk and she licked her lips nervously, prepared to tackle him as soon as possible, and get it over with, before she changed her mind. He glanced up suddenly and caught her eye, one brow flicked upwards, as if in query.

'You look delicious in that dress,' he told her, and Cadie swallowed hard on the opening words she had ready.

'Thank you.'

'Are you ready for the bright lights with Gordon?' he asked. 'Or are you out to dazzle me for some reason?'

She felt the warm flush of colour in her face and shook her head hastily. It was going to be much harder even than she had anticipated, especially now he had passed that remark about her dress.

'Neither,' she said. 'It's – it's just a dress.'

'It's nothing of the sort,' he argued with a knowing

grin. 'It's a dress with a purpose in life other than acting as mere covering. It makes you look like Scheherazade again, and you know what that does to my blood pressure. Are you sure you're not trying to dazzle me?'

'Quite sure,' Cadie assured him flatly. 'Why should I be?'

'Ah, well now, being a mere male, I wouldn't know.'

She could not resist it, and a smile curved her mouth as she cast him a look from under her lashes. 'I'm surprised to hear you using that particular adjective to describe your own sex,' she told him, and he pursed his lips thoughtfully, leaning back with his chair on only two legs.

'I'm looking at it from your angle,' he explained calmly. 'While I try and sort out your reasons for wearing that dress.'

'Oh, for heaven's sake!' Cadie exclaimed. 'Must you keep *on* about this dress? I just – just put it on, that's all, there's no ulterior motive in it.'

She might not have spoken for all the notice he took of her protest. 'Let me see.' He pressed his fingers together in a steeple and leaned back his head, looking at her from under half closed lids. 'Could it be something to do with you wanting to stay on in this job?'

She looked at him wide-eyed, but suspicious, her hands making tight little fists on top of the typewriter. It was possible that Gordon had said something to him, but if he had why didn't he come straight out and say so? Or maybe that was not devious enough for him.

'I – I don't know what you mean.'

'No?'

'No.'

'Oh. I rather thought you might have made yourself look as sexy as possible to try and get me to go on bended knee and ask you to stay with me.' He laughed. 'I *am* disappointed, my sweet!'

'What – what made you think I'd suddenly back down?' she asked suspiciously, feeling her good intentions slipping further away all the time.

'I dunno,' he shrugged, with a sly grin. 'Maybe because you don't really want to go at all.' He looked across at her steadily, a hint of smile round his mouth that was as provoking as possible. 'You don't, do you, Cadie?'

She sat there for a minute, reluctant to admit it, although Dottie would surely have pointed out that it was a heaven-sent opportunity to tell him how she felt. She looked down at her hands and slowly unclenched them. 'I don't want to leave Gordon,' she said. 'That's not quite the same thing, is it?'

'Not quite,' he agreed, and seemed to be waiting for her to go on.

'I—' She glanced up then and found the light grey eyes fixed on her with a disturbing intensity. Also he was smiling and for a moment she simply gazed at him, then realization dawned. He was doing his best to make her ask to stay on and he would then, probably, generously allow her to. The thought of his graciously accepting her plea was too much to swallow and she stuck out her chin. 'Nothing's really different, is it?' she said.

'You're still digging your heels in!'

'Aren't you?'

He laughed shortly and shook his head. 'I think I have every right to,' he said. 'After all, *you* gave notice – *I* didn't. I don't see why I should be the one to surrender.'

Cadie looked at him, frustration and anger fighting for the upper hand. 'Oh, you – ! Of all the – and to think that I was prepared this morning to – to ask you if—'

'If I'd take you back?' he guessed, and smiled. 'And Gordon said you never would.'

'I haven't asked you,' she reminded him.

'Oh, but you will.' He let his chair down on to its front legs with a bang that startled her, and leaned forward to rest his chin on clasped hands. 'You will, won't you, my sweet? That dress is much too good to waste.'

Cadie looked at him a moment longer, struggling with her injured pride that hated the very idea of begging, especially when he was so obviously enjoying the situation. At least she told herself he was, although in all fairness he was serious enough at the moment. Then she drew a deep breath and tightened her hands into fists again. 'I – I want to stay on,' she told him huskily, and he looked at her expectantly, waiting for more. 'Oh, why do you have to be such a – a tyrant?' she demanded, her eyes deep blue and blazing angrily at him. 'I want to stay because of Gordon. If it wasn't for him I'd – I'd—'

'Steady,' he warned with a grin. 'Or you'll be back

to square one again.'

'Oh – oh, go to hell!'

'Tch, tch! Not a very ladylike suggestion.' He shook his head at her. 'I'm sure Gordon never sees this side of you, does he?'

'He never drives me to it like you do,' she retorted, and banged at the typewriter keys determinedly. She had asked him, but he had still not actually agreed, and she was certainly not going to take her pleas any further.

'Do I take it that you're staying with me?' he asked, and she could tell without looking at him that he was finding it all very amusing.

She looked up, a small, discouraging frown between her brows. 'That,' she told him stiffly, 'is up to you, of course.'

'Ooh – Cadie!' He got up from his desk and came across to hers, taking her restless hands and pulling her to her feet. 'Can't you just give one little inch?' he asked softly, and she dare not look at him again because of the way her heart was panicking at his being so near. He held her two hands under his own, pressed against his chest, his blond head bent over her. 'Cadie? Look at me.'

She raised her head at last and looked at him and before she realized his intention, he bent closer and kissed her. She heard the door open behind him and felt his hands tighten on hers, then he turned his head and smiled at Gordon, releasing her at the same moment and stepping back.

'Gordon!'

Her cry was too late to stop the fist that cracked against Robert's jaw and she stared aghast at the way his head jerked from the blow. He shook his head, as if to clear it, then unbelievably he was smiling again, albeit ruefully, one hand rubbing his jaw.

'You should have an early warning system on that right of yours,' he told his stepbrother, surprisingly calm, although she thought she detected a glint of something in his eyes.

'I should give you a damned good hiding,' Gordon snapped, his face flushed and angry, his nice brown eyes hard and glittering.

Robert smiled again, wryly. 'I wouldn't advise you to try it,' he said quietly. 'You know you could never lick me, Gordon.'

'You—'

'Gordon, please!' Cadie stepped forward and put a hand on his arm, her eyes pleading. 'Please don't! There's no reason for you to be so angry, truly there isn't.'

He looked at her with that unfamiliar hardness still in his eyes, and she wondered for a minute if she had left it too late to ask for her job back. Perhaps he would not forgive this last imagined slight so easily.

'Do I take it that you were a *willing* partner?' he asked, and she shook her head hastily.

'No, I wasn't. But it still wasn't anything to make so much fuss about – especially hitting Rob like that.' She looked at him from under the heavy fringe of her lashes. 'I hope I won't be sorry I've asked for my job back, Gordon.'

'You're – you're staying on?' He brightened visibly at that, but he still cast suspicious glances at Robert, rubbing his jaw.

Cadie nodded. 'Rob says I can.'

'And that brief, chaste kiss you went off the deep end about was no more than mutual congratulations,' Robert informed him.

'Oh. Oh, I see. Well, thank goodness *that's* all over.'

'And you see there's nothing to make a fuss about,' Cadie said brightly.

He looked disinclined to be *that* certain, but at least he was a bit less angry, and Robert smiled as he walked over to his own desk. 'Now that little drama's over,' he said, 'perhaps we can get down to some work.' He looked back at Gordon curiously. 'Was it coincidence or intuition that brought you in here?' he asked him.

Gordon walked over to him – still unrepentant, still suspicious. 'There was a phone call from Commander Grove,' he told Robert. 'About the race a week on Sunday. He wondered who was crewing for you.'

Robert leaned back in his chair, one brow raised quizzically. '*You* are, I hope,' he told him.

Gordon nodded jerkily. 'That's O.K.'

'Good!' Robert grinned, a shamelessly persuasive grin, and thumped a friendly fist into his stepbrother's ribs. 'I'd rather trust you in a crisis than Lida.'

Gordon looked at him for a moment in silence, then sighed. 'O.K.,' he said slowly. 'I'm sorry I hit you. I believe you were just – well, congratulating each other on ending that damned silly feud. Now perhaps we'll get some peace around here. Right?'

Robert grinned. 'Right,' he said.

'He takes the prize for sheer cheek,' Cadie said, and Dottie smiled knowingly. 'Gordon didn't even hesitate, he just sighed and gave in, even apologized for punching him.'

'Well, so he should have done,' Dottie said, indignantly. 'Poor Rob!'

'Poor Rob!' Cadie laughed shortly. 'You have to be joking, Dottie. You don't *have* to feel sorry for Robert Dean, he's well able to take care of himself.'

Dottie looked at her with a small, sly smile round her mouth. '*Was* it just a congratulatory kiss?' she asked, and Cadie kept her eyes lowered.

'In a way.'

'Only in a way.'

'Well, I *had* just been told I could stay on,' Cadie reminded her. 'And you know Rob, he can never resist making a major issue out of everything.'

Dottie giggled. 'Nothing was ever *that* major while I was with him,' she said. 'I only wish it had been.' She eyed Cadie speculatively for a second. 'Has he kissed you before?' she asked, and Cadie felt the colour in her face, betraying her even if she did deny it.

'A couple of times,' she admitted reluctantly.

Dottie's brows danced a jig in her round face. 'And were they by way of being congratulations too?' she asked, and laughed, reaching out a hand to cover Cadie's. 'Oh, don't take any notice of me, love, I'm just green-eyed.'

'Well, you have no need to be.'

'Not much!' Dottie retorted inelegantly. 'I can imagine being kissed by Rob is just about next door to heaven.'

'Really!' Cadie scolded her, only half seriously. 'I've a good mind to tell on you to Michael.'

Dottie giggled again. 'Go ahead,' she told her. 'He knows I was crackers about Rob before I met *him*. But unlike you, I recognized that my passion was likely to be permanently unrequited, and I never was a gal to waste my time on lost causes.'

Cadie stared at her for a moment when her words sank in. 'I hope you're not suggesting that *I* nurse a passion for him too,' she said, and Dottie eyed her knowingly.

'Don't you?' she asked.

'I never thought it would happen, I have to admit.' Gordon was perched on the very edge of the kitchen table in Cadie's little cottage, watching her as she made coffee for them both, and she turned and smiled at him briefly, unwilling to have the subject raised again.

'I thought it never would, either,' she said.

'But you're not sorry you asked?'

'Not at the moment,' Cadie admitted. 'Although there have been moments during the last couple of days when I *have* been sorry. I suppose I'm just being hyper-sensitive, but it's seemed to me that he's been more annoying than ever sometimes, ever since I asked to stay on.'

'Has he?' He looked doubtful. 'Well, if he gets too

much of a good thing, darling, let me know and I'll settle him once and for all.'

'By punching him on the jaw?' Cadie asked, with uncharacteristic malice, and Gordon flushed, looking rather hurt for a moment.

'That,' he said reproachfully, 'was well below the belt, Cadie.'

'I'm sorry.'

'If you were to say you'd marry me,' he told her with a sly glance to judge her reaction, 'I'd have firmer ground to stand on when I told him.'

Cadie smiled, shaking her head as she turned with the pot of coffee. 'There's no need to say anything to him at all,' she said. 'I can manage him, Gordon, thank you.'

He sighed, taking the loaded tray from her and leading the way into her tiny sitting-room. 'O.K., have it your way.' He stood the tray down and seated himself in one of the armchairs, facing her. 'I'm wondering how he's going to explain the change of mind to Lida,' he said. 'She's coming down today.'

'To go sailing?'

He shrugged. 'Who knows?'

Cadie carefully poured him out coffee, not looking at him. 'Does he have to explain to her?' she asked.

Again he shrugged. 'I suppose so. She's bound to want to know why you're still there when the month's up, so he'll tell her I imagine. Lida never gives up.'

She glanced at him curiously. 'In what direction?'

'About marrying Rob, of course,' he said. 'You can bank on it that it's pretty certain sooner or later.'

'I see.'

He seemed fascinated with the idea for the moment. 'I have a strong suspicion he's weakening at last,' he mused. 'He's – I don't know, quite – different somehow. Nothing I can put my finger on, but—' He stopped, sipping his coffee and hastily looked down when she looked at him. 'Never mind,' he muttered, obviously embarrassed. 'I wasn't meant to see, anyway.'

'See?' Curiosity prompted her, but there was something else as well. A kind of chilling sensation that refused to be banished, when she thought of Mellida Dawson and Rob.

'It was yesterday, when you'd gone to lunch,' he told her. 'I went into the office and – and caught Rob unawares.'

'With Miss Dawson?' That could surely not have been so unusual as to cause comment.

'No, no! With—' Again he stopped in mid-sentence and shook his head, resorting to another long drink from his coffee to disguise his temptation to tell.

'Oh, Gordon, you're being absolutely maddening!' Cadie made no attempt to disguise her anxiety to hear it all now, and she put down her cup and looked at him across the few feet that separated them, her blue eyes wide with curiosity and appeal.

'I'm sorry, darling,' he apologized, seeing himself led into a corner whether he had meant to or not. 'But I *wasn't* meant to see what I did, and I haven't any right to say anything about it, not even to you. It's Rob's business – his and Lida's.

'I see.' He took her sudden quiet withdrawal as a reproach for his reticence, and leaned forward, putting down his own cup and taking her two hands in his.

'I'm sorry, darling!' He held her hands tightly for a moment and then shook his head impatiently. 'Oh, what does it matter?' he said shortly. 'I know you won't breathe a word, until it becomes public knowledge, will you?'

'I've been a confidential secretary long enough to know how to keep quiet about *any*thing,' she informed him, 'but I don't want you to betray a confidence that concerns Rob unless you know he wouldn't mind my knowing.'

'I'm sure he wouldn't,' he said, having seemingly made up his mind. 'When I came into the room, he didn't hear me and he was holding something in his hand, studying it and sort of smiling, in that secret sort of way he has sometimes.' Cadie knew just the smile he referred to, and nodded her head. 'He had a box – you know, the sort of little square box that jewellers put rings into. I saw the ring when he closed the box, in an unexpected panic, because he realized I'd seen it. It was a massive great sapphire – he's bought Lida an engagement ring.'

CHAPTER TEN

CADIE found not telling Dottie what she had learned, very hard to do. Several times she was tempted during the following week, to tell her that Robert had at last met his match, and that Mellida Dawson would soon be wearing a huge sapphire on her left hand. Gordon seemed quite delighted about it, and his reasons were obvious, for he evidently saw in it the end of his need for jealousy where Cadie was concerned. He was now busily engaged in trying to get Cadie to agree to make it a double match, but she found she had no heart for it.

She watched Robert surreptitiously all the following week, wondering what Gordon had seen in him that was different from his normal self, or if Robert himself would give away anything either deliberately or accidentally. He seemed no different, although he was perhaps a little preoccupied, but in view of the fact that he was nearing completion of a play it was not too surprising. He took his work far more seriously than he did anything else.

By Friday afternoon he had finished and handed over the last pages of manuscript to be typed. 'That,' he announced as he flopped the untidy pages in front of her, 'is that.'

'You sound as if you're glad it's over,' Cadie ventured. 'I thought you enjoyed your work.'

'So I do,' he grinned at her as he sat on the end of her desk, thus bringing her to a standstill. 'But I've got my mind on other things at the moment, and I was finding it rather hard to concentrate.'

'Oh yes – yes, of course.' She thought guiltily of the secret Gordon had betrayed to her and was not really surprised when Robert looked at her with a kind of quizzical curiosity in his eyes.

'I have a feeling we're not thinking along the same lines at the moment,' he ventured, his mouth crooked at one corner, and Cadie hastily lowered her eyes. 'What do *you* think I've got on my mind?' he asked.

'Oh!' She sought desperately for a reason – something it was reasonable for her to know about that was preoccupying him. 'The race,' she said at last, sounding rather breathless. 'The boat race on Sunday – you're very keen to win that, aren't you?'

'Ah yes, the boat race.' He laughed softly, and flicked the paper holder on her machine with a loud and irritating persistence, until she put a hand over it. 'Sorry.' He laughed again and shook his head when she met his eyes briefly. 'You're jumpy, my sweet, I wonder why.'

'I'm nothing of the sort,' Cadie denied. 'It's just that that silly noise is maddening, that's all. And if you go on sitting there I can't get on and finish my typing.'

'Not to worry,' he told her blithely, staying where he was. 'You can always come in tomorrow and finish it.'

She looked at him suspiciously, wondering if he was serious about it. She was not normally required to work on Saturdays, and she hoped she would not have to this time. 'There'll be no need for me to come in, if you let me get on with it now,' she said.

'I pay good overtime rates.' He still sounded as if he was teasing her, but she could still not be sure if he meant it or not. 'Double time on Saturdays,' he added by way of an added incentive.

'I don't work on Saturdays,' she told him, a hasty glance revealing the firm set of his jaw.

'You do if I want you to,' he informed her quietly. 'That was in the agreement you signed.'

Cadie blinked for a moment, suspicious of his motives. 'I don't remember signing anything like that,' she told him, and he grinned knowingly.

'Funny how no one ever reads the small print on *any*thing they're given to sign,' he said. 'They just scribble away quite happily, trusting the other fellow to be honest.'

'It's not a bad trait, to trust others,' Cadie told him defensively, still not convinced.

'If you don't believe me, and I can see you don't, I can show you the actual paper with your signature attached,' he offered, but Cadie shook her head.

She did not doubt he would be proved right, in fact it was a foregone conclusion, but she wished she *had* read the contract of employment she had so blithely signed for Gordon. She had not expected anyone in their profession to be so practical as to cover things like overtime when it was required, but she should have known better, she thought ruefully.

'I believe you,' she allowed. 'But I don't see why I

should have to give up my week-end when it's your fault I can't get on with the job.' She banged down the carriage release and sent it flying along until it met his leg with a thud that made him move hastily away.

'You little fiend!' he declared, and Cadie smiled her triumph as she began typing again.

'Now perhaps I can get on and finish,' she said.

'I could sue you for assault,' he told her, rubbing his leg. 'Do you realize that?'

'Assault with a deadly weapon?' she suggested, with a smile. 'I don't think so, Rob. Just think of the defence I could put up – especially with you.'

'And you would too, wouldn't you?' he asked softly, a gleam in his eyes that she missed because she merely nodded and kept her fingers busy without looking up.

'I'm not going to have my Saturday spoiled without doing something about it,' she informed him.

'I suppose you're seeing Gordon?'

'That's right.'

'As usual!' His tone surprised her and she glanced up hastily, but he was already half-way back to his desk and she could not see his face.

She said nothing, but felt an uneasy, disturbing thudding in the region of her heart as she tried to concentrate on the words she was typing. What right had he to sound so annoyed about her spending Saturday with Gordon when he was about to become engaged to Mellida Dawson? Really, he was a prime example of a man wanting to have his cake and eat it too!

She found it much more difficult now to keep her

mind on what she was doing, especially as he sat at his own desk gazing out of the window, uncharacteristically idle. She could sense the tense alertness of him, even across the room, although he gave the appearance of being relaxed. A feeling almost of excitement and, inevitably, she glanced across at him, watching him for several seconds until he turned his head, drawn by her scrutiny.

One brow flicked upwards into the blond thatch over his forehead and his mouth crooked wryly. 'What's wrong, my sweet?' he asked softly, and Cadie drew an involuntary breath, hastily lowering her eyes.

'Nothing,' she said. 'Nothing, of course.'

'Of course,' he echoed mockingly, and laughed. She went back to her typing, but she was aware now that he was watching her instead of the scene outside the window, and tried to control the sudden clumsiness of her fingers. 'Are you coming to watch me sail on Sunday?' he asked then.

'I – I might,' she said, not looking at him. 'Gordon did ask me if I'd like to.'

'Oh yes, of course – you'll be watching him, won't you?'

His tone again puzzled her and she looked at him with a small puzzled frown between her brows. 'I don't understand you,' she said after a moment or two. 'You sound as if – as if you don't like me watching Gordon sail.'

'*I* don't mind,' he told her with a wry grin, 'as long as he doesn't start playing to your gallery and ruin my chances by showing off.'

Cadie flushed. 'It's unlikely he'll let you down,' she said. 'He never has yet, has he?'

'Not yet,' he agreed solemnly. 'But then I've never had to compete with you before.'

'Oh, Rob, for heaven's sake!' She gave up any pretence of working and sat and looked at him with wide and curious eyes.

He met her gaze quite seriously for a moment, then the inevitable grin appeared and he ran a hand through his hair. 'O.K., my sweet, I shouldn't make snide remarks about you and Gordon. I apologize.'

'So you should,' Cadie retorted. 'Especially when you're going—' She bit back the indiscretion that had so nearly been voiced and hastily looked down at her work again, although all she saw was a jumble of words which made no sense so that it was pointless trying to type them.

'I'm going to what?' he asked softly, and got up from his desk again so that Cadie bit her lip and tried to stop the rapid hammering in her breast.

'I didn't—' She got no further, but heaved an almost audible sigh of relief when the door opened to admit Gordon.

He looked from one to the other of them for a second, his eyes suspicious as usual whenever he saw them together, and Cadie saw the way Robert's mouth contracted into an uncharacteristic thin line as he turned towards his stepbrother.

'Now what?' he asked brusquely, so that Gordon blinked at him for a moment.

'Sorry to butt in,' he said. 'But Sam's on the phone wanting to know if you've completed that last piece yet.'

Robert nodded. 'We have,' he said. 'At least I have, it still has to be typed, but tell him it'll be in the post tonight.'

'Right.' He glanced again at the two of them, then withdrew, leaving a kind of uneasy silence in the room which Robert broke when he walked back to his own desk.

'That means you'll *have* to finish it tonight,' he said. 'I'll leave you to get on with it in peace.' He made some small show of tidying his desk, then shrugged and went to the door. 'I feel like a breath of air,' he told her. 'Sorry I can't ask you to join me, but you heard what the man said.'

'I – I don't mind in the least,' Cadie told him quietly. 'I can finish it easily this afternoon.'

He grinned ironically at her over one shoulder as he opened the door. 'If I leave you in peace,' he said, and went out of the room, leaving Cadie with a strange and uneasy feeling that something, somewhere was changing much too quickly for her to keep pace with it.

Sunday was a fine bright day again, and ideal for sailing because there was a good offshore breeze blowing as well that would make it more of a race. That much knowledge Cadie had picked up from Gordon, although he spoke little about sailing and she sometimes suspected that he did not altogether share his stepbrother's enthusiasm for it.

She lay for quite a long while before she got up, letting her mind wander all over the place, and was surprised to find herself wondering who it was she was really going to watch this afternoon. Certainly she had promised Gordon she would be watching, but frequently and disturbingly she found her thoughts straying instead to Robert's part in it.

She remembered her own brief time aboard the small graceful boat and she had noticed then that its name was *Enchantress*. She wondered now if the enchantress referred to Mellida Dawson or if Robert had merely named his boat for her own sake. Strange, she thought, how men always referred to boats and cars as feminine. No doubt there was a Freudian answer to it, but she was not prepared to worry about that at the moment.

She called in to see Dottie and Michael after lunch, wondering if they had decided to watch too, but Dottie shook her head, albeit regretfully. 'It's too hot, love,' she said. 'I'd only pass out or do something equally daft and be a nuisance to everybody.' She glanced at her husband affectionately. 'I've tried to persuade Michael to go, but he won't leave me for some reason or other.'

'I don't trust you not to get up to something you shouldn't while I'm out of the way,' Michael told her with a smile, and Dottie stuck out her tongue at him. They were, Cadie thought, just a little wistfully, so marvellously happy together.

'It's a gorgeous sight,' Dottie was telling her. 'Seeing them all come round the headland. We watched them last year, and you can see them all sweeping round the marker buoy there. All – ooh, I don't know – it makes my toes tingle to see them. Beautiful and graceful, like dancers.'

'You're waxing quite poetic,' Cadie teased.

'All right, laugh,' Dottie said indignantly. 'But you wait till you see about a dozen or eighteen little sail boats coming round the headland, with the sun shining and the blue sky and the sea. *You*'ll wax poetic, I'll bet you any money. Especially,' she added with a sly grin, 'if your boss is leading the way.'

'Does he stand a chance of leading the way?' Cadie asked, studying the tips of her fingers, and Dottie nodded vigorously.

'Everyone seems to think he does,' she said. 'The odds are very short on him at the moment.'

Cadie looked up and blinked. 'You mean people bet on the race?'

'Sure they do,' Dottie grinned. 'Mr. Daly, the betting shop man on the Dorfleet road, always runs a book on it. Everybody has a flutter.'

'Even you?'

Dottie nodded. 'Of course. We've put our money on Rob, even if the odds are short.' She cocked her head to one side, her big eyes sparkling mischief. 'Aren't you tempted?' she asked. 'You might double your salary.'

Cadie laughed. 'I'm not tempted to that extent,' she told her. 'Anyway I haven't time to do anything about it before the race starts.' She got up from her chair. 'I'd better be going if I'm to see the finish of this epic race.'

Dottie walked with her to the door. 'Who're you cheering for?' she asked, and Cadie smiled.

'*Enchantress*,' she told her, and laughed at Dottie's moue of reproach.

She had never seen so many people about at one time in Dorly Creek, and there were cars parked in every available space along the quay and the sandy stretch of the bay. Cadie sought somewhere a little less crowded, and so she made her way further round towards the headland, where she and Gordon had so often sat, only now she stayed on the lower level of the beach.

It was quiet here because most of the crowd stayed near the start and finish, and she sat in the welcome shade of an overhang from the headland. The sand was warm and soft and the sun glittered on the sea, with only a light wind disturbing its surface. Even so she experienced some of the same excitement that infected the crowds on the quay, sitting there alone on the deserted beach, hugging her knees and waiting for the first sail to come into sight.

Many of the little boats would look alike, she knew, even though each had its own number marked on a sail, but she would surely recognize Robert's blond head as she had done when he came to her rescue at Dorly Point.

Annoyingly she found herself thinking again about Robert and Mellida Dawson, as she sat with her chin resting on her clasped hands. Maybe they would celebrate this success today by getting engaged. Impatiently she shrugged off the nagging dislike that persisted whenever she thought of that engagement.

Perhaps it would have been a better idea to have left after all, for she could not easily face the idea of Mellida Dawson flaunting that huge sapphire every time she came to Dorly House, and she would surely come more often now, when they were officially engaged.

She had taken little notice of the passing time as she sat there, so that she was taken almost by surprise when the first white sails appeared round the headland, dipping and bowing gracefully before the breeze. The breeze that was much brisker now that it had been when the race started, and more variable as it changed with the outline of the coast and the eddying hollows in the headland. The crews were busier on the small boats, ducking and bobbing as they changed position constantly.

They *were* beautiful, Cadie thought, as she watched them. She could easily grow as poetic as Dottie had been, watching the white sails billowing against the blue sky, hulls shiny and gleaming, with the rippling sea dancing around them and doing its best to upset their precarious balance.

It was like some lovely picture come to life and a sight not easily forgotten. There were three of them very close together as they came round the first buoy, and Cadie shielded her eyes as she searched for a familiar blond head, her heart leaping crazily when she spotted it in the second of the three.

It needed all the skill and experience of the busy crews as the breeze skimmed and shifted past the headland, and she found herself on her feet, watching anxiously as the first two boats jostled for priority round the buoy. Her hands were clasped together and she put them up to her mouth as the shiny, gleaming *Enchantress* slipped past her rival and dipped her sails mockingly, it seemed – a gesture that reminded Cadie so much of the boat's owner that she laughed delightedly.

The other boat, however, was close on her heels and Cadie danced her impatience, willing the gap between them to widen. It had not occurred to her that she too was visible, as a minute figure on the lonely beach, but she sensed suddenly that she had been seen, and a second later a hand fluttered briefly on the leading boat and, instinctively, she responded.

What happened next was so sudden and so unexpected that she could scarcely believe she had seen it for a moment. One minute she could see Robert's blond head clearly and the next minute a wildly swinging boom caught it a blow that knocked him off his feet and over the side.

'Rob!'

She stood with her hands to her mouth, her eyes wide, for the moment the whole world seeming to have stopped, then she ran to the very edge of the water, staring at the tiny, bright orange speck that was his lifejacket. She was vaguely aware that Gordon was trying to come about, but threatening to capsize as he did so – threatening too to bring chaos to the following boats if he was not very careful.

Cadie never knew what possessed her in that

moment, only that Robert was out there in the water after a bang on the head that must surely have knocked him unconscious. Without pausing to think she flung down her handbag and kicked off her shoes, then ran into the water, swimming strongly towards that bobbing orange speck.

She was obliged to pause for a second after a while and get her bearings, and she noticed with relief that the rest of the boats had passed him safely and he was now nearer to her than she had expected. Evidently he was drifting inshore on the wash.

It was further out than she had realized, and she began to tire suddenly, before she reached him, feeling her arms and legs grow heavy, and only vaguely aware that the *Enchantress* with Gordon on board was much closer to Robert than she was. She was gasping for breath and wondering if Gordon had seen her. She trod water for a second, then felt a sudden cold panic again when she remembered that bang on the head she had witnessed.

'Rob!'

Her voice sounded strangely flat and dead just above the water and she swallowed a great mouthful and almost choked on it. She raised her head as best she could and peered across the rippling green surface to where she thought Rob should be. The *Enchantress* was bobbing peacefully only a few yards away from her and she thought Gordon was already hauling his step-brother over the side, only she had too little time to judge properly.

Her own breath was painfully short and she felt like

giving up, but that would do no good at all, and surely Gordon would have seen her by now. Sure enough she saw his anxious and surprised face turned in her direction and, moments later, hands reached down for her. It was as she was pulled into the boat that she fainted and lay in a bedraggled heap with her long hair clinging like seaweed to her face and neck.

Cadie opened her eyes cautiously, the sun dazzling her for a moment, so that she hastily closed them again. When she looked up again, however, someone was blocking the sun; a blond head, now darkly wet from a ducking, and a brown face with light grey eyes and a smile that was at once anxious and reassuring. Her hands were held, tightly, by two strong brown ones, and she stared at him for a moment in disbelief.

'Rob!'

'In person,' he said. 'Are you surprised?'

'But I thought—' She closed her eyes and shook her head, colour flooding into her pale cheeks when she realized how unnecessary her panic had been. He had been in no danger of drowning, for one thing because he had been wearing a life-jacket, although he had discarded it now. The blow she had thought so serious must merely have been a glancing one and had not even knocked him unconscious. What an idiot he must think her!

'You thought what, my sweet?' He really had no right, she thought in a panic as her heart skipped wildly, to sound so gentle and – yes, seductive was the word. Not when he was planning to put that huge sapphire on Mellida Dawson's finger.

'I – I saw – I thought I saw you hit your head,' she whispered huskily, her throat horribly dry and salty.

He grinned then, rubbing his left temple with one hand. 'You saw a rotten bit of seamanship,' he told her. 'Comes of having the crew distracted by beautiful sirens on shore!'

Realization dawned then, and she noticed Gordon for the first time. He sat in the stern only just in her view and looking rather sulkily resentful. 'Gordon—' she began, but Robert recaptured her attention determinedly.

'Gordon took his mind off the job for a vital second,' he told her. 'Just think what you were responsible for, Cadie O'Connor! A lost race, a crack on my head and your own near drowning.'

'But it *wasn't* my fault,' Cadie objected, almost automatically. She looked up at him soulfully, her eyes wide and deeply blue. 'Have we – have you lost the race completely?' she asked, and he nodded.

'Last in,' he informed her, sounding far less annoyed about it than she would have expected.

'I'm sorry.'

'No doubt the local bookie will be quite happy,' he told her cheerfully, 'but poor old Dottie's lost her shirt. She was gambling her all on me, I gather.' He cocked a quizzical brow at her. 'Did you bet on me?'

Cadie shook her head. 'No, I didn't have time.'

'Huh! Loyalty!' He helped her to sit up, one hand pushing back the wet hair from her face, his eyes gently curious. 'What puzzles me,' he said slowly, 'is how you came to be swimming about out there in your clothes.'

'I—' She bit her lip, hating to have to explain the cold unreasoning panic that had sent her into the water without stopping to think of the consequences. Glancing guiltily at Gordon, she bit her lip. 'I – I thought you were – I mean I didn't know—'

He silenced her by the simple expedient of kissing her, and she felt that wild, illogical skip in her heart again as he held her hands. 'Bless you, my sweet,' he said softly, and with indescribable gentleness. 'You came to rescue me, didn't you?'

'I daren't go in this morning,' Cadie confided to Dottie via the telephone. 'I'm late as it is. Dottie, what am I going to say to him? I feel such a fool.'

'There's no need,' Dottie assured her blithely. 'You just go in as usual, love, and see how he is this morning.'

'Oh, he wasn't badly hurt, that's just the trouble,' Cadie said, and heard her friend chuckle.

'I don't think you meant that,' she said, 'any more than I meant his bump on the head. I was referring to a region a bit lower down – like the heart, for instance.'

'Oh, Dottie, for heaven's sake! You never give up, do you?'

'Not while there's a spark of hope,' Dottie assured her with another chuckle. 'After all, love, he's bound to be touched by your gesture of self-sacrifice, isn't he?'

'That's nonsense,' Cadie objected.

'Not nonsense at all,' Dottie insisted, sticking to her guns. 'It's not every woman would plunge into the ocean when she sees her – her—'

'Dottie!'

'Well, it isn't,' Dottie ended with a chuckle.

'You're as bent on making a mountain out of a mole-hill as Gordon was,' Cadie told her. 'He said barely a word all the way back, and it was Rob brought me home.'

'Didn't you see him last night? Gordon, I mean.'

'No. He said – he said he didn't feel like going out again.' She shrugged, finding herself not as troubled by Gordon's obvious sulking as she would once have been. 'I suppose I had to expect a change of heart with Gordon sooner or later.'

Dottie made vaguely sympathetic noises over the telephone. 'He is a bit fickle, love. If you remember, Rob warned you he was.'

'I remember.'

She was feeling very gloomy and unsure of herself this morning one way and another. That was why she had rung Dottie so early in the morning, knowing her to be an early riser. She needed someone to confide in.

Her future at Dorly House looked far from bright this morning. With Gordon more or less dropping her like a hot brick, and Robert about to become engaged to Mellida Dawson, it was not a bright prospect at all. She heaved a great sight of resignation, and looked at her watch. 'Oh well, I'd better show my face, I suppose,' she said. 'Thanks for listening, Dottie.'

The very first person Cadie saw when she walked into the hall at Dorly House was Gordon, and she looked at him for a moment, wondering if he would want to speak to her this morning. He glanced at the door of the office, almost warily, she thought, then came acrosss to her, his brown eyes looking more reproachful than anything else this morning.

'Cadie!'

'Hello, Gordon.'

She wondered just how friendly she should appear.

'I – I hope you didn't think too badly of me yesterday.'

She looked at him curiously for a second. 'Why should I think badly of you?' she asked, deciding to ignore the sulky way he had behaved on the return journey.

'I mean – well—' He held his hands tightly together and looked rather like a schoolboy who has been caught out in some misdemeanour. 'I still feel as I always have about you, Cadie, you know that, but – well, Rob explained, and I won't make a fuss, I promise.'

Cadie looked at him for a moment in silence, unsure whether the feeling that seethed through her was anger or elation. 'I don't think I understand, Gordon,' she told him, trying to steady her voice when it quavered and threatened to crack.

He looked at her in turn, his expression part puzzled, part suspicious. 'I mean you don't have to worry that I'll make a fuss about you and Robert,' he said slowly, and Cadie drew a deep breath, but before she could give voice to anything at all the door of the office opened and Robert stood in the doorway.

'Good morning, Cadie!'

She turned and looked at him, a strange and inexplicable trembling in her limbs, while Gordon murmured a hasty word of good-bye and disappeared across the hall as if he had been forbidden to speak to her. After a moment she moved across to the office, her hands clenched tightly into small fists as she glared at him suspiciously.

'What have you been saying to Gordon?' she demanded, and shrugged her shoulders as he pushed her in to the room and closed the door. 'Don't push!'

He regarded her for a moment with bright, quizzical eyes, leaning against the closed door with his arms folded across his chest. 'Are we in one of our militant moods this morning?' he asked, apparently undeterred by the fact.

'I wasn't until I saw Gordon,' she told him shortly, and wished there was something she could do about the alarming rate of her pulse.

'Oh, I see.' He pushed himself away from the door and walked over to his desk.

'I'd like you to explain, if you don't mind. Gordon seems to have taken fright at the sight of you, and I didn't have a chance to ask him what he meant.'

'About what?'

She walked round the other side of his desk and faced him, her heart thudding frantically hard against her ribs. 'That's just it, I don't know.'

'Are you feeling all right after yesterday's little drama?' he asked, and she frowned.

'Yes, thank you. Rob, don't change the subject.'

'I wasn't.'

She took a very deep breath and tightened her fists, determined to get to the bottom of whatever it was he had told Gordon. 'What have you been saying to Gordon to make him – to make him—'

'Shy off?' he suggested softly, and laughed.

It was really very difficult to think straight about anything when he looked at her like that. A kind of gentle, exciting challenge in his light eyes as he gazed at her mouth in fascination. 'Rob!'

'I shall have to remember to duck you in salt water every so often,' he told her softly. 'You look more beautiful even than usual this morning.'

'Will you be serious?'

'You think I'm not?' He came round to her, and stood only inches away, smiling in a slow, inviting way that sent a shiver of excitement, perhaps even panic, along her spine. He took her hands in his first and raised her fingers to his lips, kissing them gently, then his hands slid down to her waist and he drew her close against him until she could feel the warmth and strength of him as he held her there.

'Rob?'

'Hmm?' He kissed her forehead gently. 'You were ready to come out and swim your heart out to rescue me, weren't you?' he asked quietly, and she nodded, instinctively, she realized, because it was true.

'You're – you're not answering me,' she told him.

'Why did you tell Gordon – whatever it was you told him about you and me?'

'You and me,' he echoed. 'That sounds right, doesn't it, Cadie?'

'I – Oh, I don't know!' she wailed. 'I wish I knew what you were doing. You – you get that ring for Miss Dawson, and now—'

He held her off for a second, one brow querying, and she realized with dismay that she had betrayed Gordon's secret he had been so pleased about. 'What ring might that be?' he asked. 'And what do you know about it?'

'If you—' She stopped, looking up at him. 'A – a sapphire ring,' she whispered guiltily. 'I know I wasn't supposed to know about it, Rob, but I didn't tell anyone else, honestly. Not even Dottie.'

'Not even Dottie!' he echoed, and hugged her close again.

'We – I naturally thought it must be for Miss Dawson,' she told him, her voice husky and barely audible.

'I can't see why naturally,' he said. 'Where Gordon got the idea from that I intended marrying Lida, I can't imagine. She's not my type.'

'But she must be,' Cadie objected, automatically. 'You've been—'

'Friends,' he told her. 'That's all, my sweet. I've had dozens of them, I frankly admit it.' He grinned down at her. 'But only because Dottie will have told you anyway,' he added. 'I knew you were something different the day you told me off for *you* bumping into *my* car.'

'You were very rude to me,' Cadie told him, smiling about it now, because it seemed rather unimportant.

'And you were such a staunch little feminist,' he said. 'You took every opportunity to preach to me how equal the sexes were, and yet you always wore dresses that emphasized the difference.' He kissed her chin and laughed softly. 'I knew one of these days you'd get fed up with fighting me and fall into the natural order of things.'

'Like letting you boss me about?' she guessed, and he grinned.

'All I had to do was sit back and wait for you to shout *"Vive la différence!"* – and fall into my arms. Mind you,' he added seriously, 'I had a few nasty moments when it looked as if you weren't going to change your mind about staying on here.'

'I – I haven't fallen into your arms,' Cadie told him, a little breathlessly, and he smiled, his blond head bent over her as he held her still closer.

'But you have,' he said, and kissed her mouth in a way that left her no room for doubt. He snuggled his face against her neck his voice muffled in the long, silky black hair. 'And sapphires match your eyes beautifully, my sweet.'

'Rob!' He kissed her again, his mouth gentle and persuasive and more exciting than anything she'd ever experienced before. 'How did you know I liked sapphires?' she asked, and he chuckled against her ear.

'I know you as well as you know yourself,' he told her. 'Better sometimes.'

'And you're always so right, aren't you?'

'Always,' he agreed, seeking her mouth again.

Cadie managed to catch a small breath at last, and looked up at him with huge, shining eyes. *'Vive la différence!'* she whispered huskily.

A Publishing Event of special interest.

The autobiography of a warm and charming woman who has become one of the most famous authors of romantic fiction in the world

The Essie Summers Story

The Essie Summers Story

One of the world's most popular and admired authors of romantic fiction, and a special favourite of all Harlequin readers, tells her story.

Essie Summers, the author of such best-selling books as "Bride in Flight," "Postscript to Yesterday," "Meet on My Ground" and "The Master of Tawhai," to name just a few, has spent two years bringing the manuscript of her autobiography to its present stage of perfection.

The wit, warmth and wisdom of this fine lady shine through every page. Her love of family and friends, of New Zealand and Britain, and of life itself, is an inspiration throughout the book. Essie Summers captures the essence of a life well lived, and lived to the fullest, in the style of narrative for which she is justly famous.

"The Essie Summers Story," published in paperback, is available at .95 a copy through Harlequin Reader Service, now!